WAS THEN...

5. (a) He's quite partial to "Toast".
   (b) He's from Luton.
   (c) His first hit was an old Marvin Gaye number which shot to number one.

6. (a) He loves motorbikes.
   (b) He's from Fife, Scotland.
   (c) He likes taking a "Chance".

7. (a) He used to be in Slik.
   (b) He's a mate of Sir Bob's.
   (c) He loves "Vienna".

8. (a) He writes poetry.
   (b) He loves quizes, especially pop ones.
   (c) His guitar playing is pretty annoying.

9. (a) He used to be a Commodore.
   (b) He's a jolly successful songwriter.
   (c) He likes saying, "Hello."

10. (a) He hasn't got quite so much hair these days.
    (b) He still wears naff shirts.
    (c) He's always bright, bouncy, enthusiastic and *really* annoying.

11. (a) He's American.
    (b) He's a drummer.
    (c) He's one of the boys in blue!

Contents

4

UPFRO

DELROY PEARSON
● The girls all regard him as their bodyguard.
● The youngest member of the family was born on April 11, 1970, making him an Arien.
● As a youngster, he nearly became a professional footballer, and was considering doing a trial with West Ham, but Stedman said the band came first.
● He loves fishing, and says it's a really relaxing hobby.
● He used to be a big fan of wildlife programmes.
● He plays drums in the group.
● His nickname is Medallion Man, because he's always wearing gold chains.
● Before the group made the big time, Delroy was worried about how he'd look on TV, because he says he's on the 'heavy' side!
● He'd love to be a successful producer/engineer.

DENIECE PEARSON
● Born Deniece Lisa Marie Pearson on June 13, 1968, she is a Gemini.
● She wasn't a big fan of school, because she didn't make any friends, but went because she was told she had a lot to learn.
● Even at a really young age she had an amazing voice, and used to sing along with groups who appeared on TV.
● As a youngster, the rest of the family thought she might become a nurse.
● She collects souvenirs of all their visits, and usually does things like pinching soap from hotels, and suchlike.
● She says her style of singing is influenced by Smokey Robinson.
● She composes all the songs, and has a set of keyboards, which are indispensible to her composing.
● She loves watching cartoons.

LORRAINE PEARSON
● Born Lorraine Samantha Jean Pearson on August 10, 1967, she's a Leo.
● As a youngster she wanted to be an actress or a writer.
● Although Doris is the major Michael Jackson devotee, it was actually Lorraine who was his original fan in the family.
● She's a brainy gal, and even did Business Studies at college.
● Her favourite actor was Cary Grant, and she loves watching his old films.
● She hates wearing make-up, especialy the heavy type they've to wear onstage and for photos.
● She keeps a scrapbook, in which she pastes every cutting about the band.
● Her dream is to have a huge house in the country, have great success as a band, and be a successful writer.

STEDMAN PEARSON
● He was born on June 29, 1964 and is a Cancerian.
● At school, he was a really athletic lad, and reckons he could have made it as a sprinter or a rugby scrum half.
● Nowadays, though, he's well-into karate.
● His hobbies include painting (the arty type, not walls), photography, and he's really into UFO's and anything to do with outer space.
● Before the group made the big time, he left home for a while, but didn't like it as he was shy and didn't know how to do things like pay rent.
● His nickname as a child was Teddy Edwards.
● He attended Barking College and studied performing arts.
● Whilst he was a student he worked as a waiter in a wine bar.
● He was an honest lad as a youngster, and if anything was ever broken during raucous games, he would step forward to take the blame.

DORIS PEARSON
● Doris is the oldest girl, and she was born on June 8, 1966, making her a Gemini subject.
● At only 5 ft. 3½ in., she's the smallest member of the family, and is affectionately known as Midget.
● Her favourite pastime at school was playing netball.
● She used to get into trouble from Mum and Dad for coming home too late.
● Her ambition is "to be perfect for the rest of my life".
● She's not really into going out and living it up, and much prefers staying at home and helping Mum do the cooking. (Wacky, huh?)
● As a youngster she was really chubby.
● She does all the choreography for the band, but as a youngster she hated going to ballet lessons because of the clothes she had to wear.
● To relax, she loves listening to old Nat King Cole records.
● She'd love to do a routine with Michael Jackson, and maybe even marry him.

Wacky, wacky, wacky! It's amazing what you can do with a hairbrush if you really try. These subdued little styles were created with the help of a Denman styling brush. Nice style, shame about the hairnet, dear . . .

We don't have anything constructive to say about them, but here's a yummy, scrummy piccy of A-Ha for you to feast your greedy little eyes on, me dears!

GLOVES

There's nothing like a pair of long black gloves to give instant sophistication to certain outfits . . . (obviously, they won't have the same effect if you sport them with jeans and a jersey). Suss Mum and Gran for authentic '50's and '60's numbers . . . Don't go overboard with gems — a classy ring is enough to complete the look . . .

6

SCARVES

Contrary to popular belief, scarves aren't just for wrappin round your head when your hair needs washing . . .

Use them to brighten up a basic outfit in the following ways . .

1. Let's start off with the neck, shall we? It's a bit too hippyish to leave the ends a-trailin', the fringes a-flowin', so wrap them round until you can wrap n more.
2. No matter what your hair's like, you can usually adorn it with a scarf or two . . . make headbands (haw! haw! hippy!), tie pretty girl bows or be really boring and tie your hair back in a scarf when it's needing a wash.
Note: to wear a scarf à la Princess Anne/your mum is UNTRENDY . . .
3. Wear it round your waist . . . tightly, like a cummerbund, or loosely, so that it's a hip-swingin' garment . . .
4. You have to be really wacky for this one . . . Scarves tied round tight black-canvas clad legs are most becoming on a lad. You may get laughed at in the street, but there you go — you have to suffer to be a trendy . . .

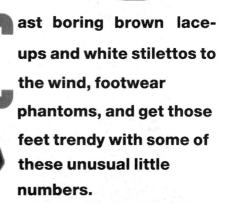

Leopardskin bootees,
from market stall.

Cast boring brown lace-ups and white stilettos to the wind, footwear phantoms, and get those feet trendy with some of these unusual little numbers.

*Rockin' boots,
from Miss Selfridge.*

Fancy being creative? Howabout running up a few wicky-wacky garments of your own design to astound everyone with at the local groove palace this weekend? It's not impossible.

Take some inspiration from this little lot, who are students at the Newcastle College of Arts and Technology. Here, they made up their best designs and sported them on the catwalk for all and sundry to see.

THE GIRL IN THE PICTURE

John and his brother had just moved in next door to Anna . . .

EM . . . IS YOUR BROTHER INTERESTED IN PHOTOGRAPHY THEN?

DAVID? HE'S NUTS ABOUT IT. YOU NEVER SEE HIM WITHOUT A CAMERA.

JUST MY LUCK. ANNA'S THE BEST-LOOKING GIRL AROUND HERE AND SHE FANCIES MY BROTHER!

The next day . . .

THERE HE GOES AGAIN—IF ONLY I HAD THE REMOTEST IDEA ABOUT PHOTOGRAPHY, I'D BE LAUGHING . . .

8

Monkey boots, from market stall.

Old-fashioned granny court shoes, from Saxone.

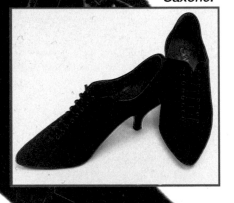

Fringed suede boots, from Schuh.

MANY years ago, in the 18th century (1730, ackcholoi), a young Spaniard by the name of Juan Famenais Floris opened up the first perfume shop in the West End of London. He introduced Spanish oils never before known to man and was also quite an adventurous sort of lad as he mixed his own perfumes.

Nowadays, perfume is big business. Such far-out ingredients as alcohol, flowers, fruit, seeds and chemicals all go towards your fave smell.

How To Choose Your Perfume . . .

● Remember, perfume smells differently on everyone, so don't assume that just because it smells great on your pal, it'll smell just as wondrous on you.

● Don't test more than four perfumes at one time — your nose will just become confused and you won't get a true smell. Leave it for about fifteen minutes so that it gets a chance to adapt to your skin — scientifically, it takes about that time for its "base" and "middle" notes to come through.

● Perfume lasts a lot longer on dry skin, so if you've got greasy skin, go for a heavier type of perfume.

● When you've found out your fave perfume, buy the lighter concentrations, like eau de toilette or cologne, rather than the perfume itself. These ones are a lot cheaper, and a lot lighter — sometimes fully-fledged perfumes are too heavy for everyday wear.

● Make sure the top or stopper is clean — any dirt or grease can damage the smell.

No gal's life is complete without an attractive little trinket box for her to store her much-loved gems in. We fell in love with this silver one at a photo-session one day. (We were actually supposed to be working hard, but just for a change we were nosing around the cupboards instead.)

Look out for trinket boxes and the like in cheapo second-hand shops. You never know what you'll find lurking amongst the granny suits and holey jerseys!

How To Look After Your Perfume . . .
● Be careful about where you keep it. Make sure you keep it somewhere cool and dark, as heat and bright sunlight can alter the chemical balance and your perfume will go off.
● Don't save perfume for special occasions — once you break the seal, it'll start to evaporate, so use it as much as possible.
● Perfume lasts a lot longer on damp skin, so the best time to apply it is when you're fresh from a steaming shower.

Amazing And Interesting Facts About Porfume . . .
● Think you've got a fairly classy, expensive pefume? Well, in November 1983, the first limited edition perfume went on sale — there are only 5000 bottles of Le Parfum Salvadore Dali, and originally they cost a mere £2,750. A snippo, eh?
● Chanel No 5 is possibly *the* most sophisticated perfume — it was first made in 1921 when the wondrous fashion designer Coco Chanel asked her lover, perfumier René Coty, to create a perfume specially for her. It took him five attempts before she was finally satisfied — so it become Chanel No.5.
● Chanel No 19 was named after Coco Chanel's birthdate, August 19.
● Marilyn Monroe was once asked in an interview what she wore in bed. "Chanel No 5" she replied.
● The French National Committee for Perfumes' motto is "Without perfume Your Skin Is Dumb".
● Selfridges of London has one of the biggest perfume departments in the country. The most expensive perfume in the country is L'Air d'Or by L'Air D'Or. A 32 ounce size bottle costs £8000.

BELTS

Belts are always

a winner for adding a

bit of interest to an

otherwise boring

outfit. Shop around

for second-hand

numbers, or cheap

bargains in the

shops.

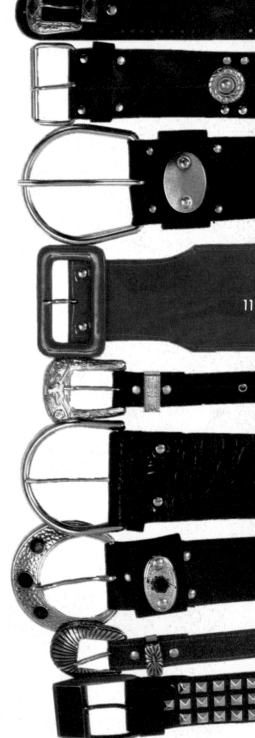

11

13

FOOD FOR THOUGHT

Two pages about everybody's favourite hobby — eating!

Food is brilliant. Not only does it keep you alive and provide you with protein and vitamins, it also tastes good — what a bonus! Everybody loves eating, so it's hardly surprising that we devote so much time to it. Breakfast, elevenses, lunch, tea, dinner, supper . . . eating can be a never-ending hobby.

The important thing about this consuming pastime is that you eat a *balanced* diet. To keep your body in good condition, you need a variety of vitamins, protein, iron and calcium, so eat lots of fresh fruit and vegetables, meat, fish and fowl. This may sound boring, but if you have a nice mixture it doesn't have to be. It's a little-known fact that most people in this country who eat regular meals — and we're talking about "common" foods, not mountains of fresh fruit and vegetables — are taking in the recommended level of vitamins needed, because almost any food will provide the human body with the amount of vitamins it requires to maintain good health. This means that it is unnecessary to supplement your diet with endless bottles of vitamin pills — they aren't needed and so are just flushed straight through the body. Keep this in mind next time you reach for your easy-to-swallow multi-vitamins. You'd be better spending the money on some nice fruit, which contains the same vitamins but tastes a whole lot nicer than a pill.

DO OR DIET . . .

A large majority of the population of Britain, and in particular the female half, will almost certainly spend some time dieting — and for what? To lose weight, in an effort to look like the pencil-thin models who stare at us from adverts on TV and in magazines. Diets are boring, take ages to show results and unless they include eating vast amounts of chocolate, are guaranteed to be not much fun. Simply by eating sensibly and exercising regularly, there's no reason why the human body shouldn't look perfectly OK. If, however, you are well overweight, consult your doctor who will be able to recommend a *safe* diet.

Certain "fad" diets may cause you to lose pounds in a matter of days, but sudden weight loss is dangerous. It may look good, but it will become difficult to maintain your new weight, unless it has been achieved slowly. A doctor will make sure your body is broken in gently to the idea of receiving less food and he/she will also keep check on the rate at which you lose weight, just to make sure things arc going OK.

FOOD IS FUN

Those Arabs certainly know how to enjoy themselves . . . The largest meal in the world is one which is occasionally cooked for Bedouin wedding feasts. Cooked eggs are stuffed into fish, the fish stuffed into cooked chickens, the chickens stuffed into a roasted sheep carcass and the sheep stuffed into a whole camel, which is roasted.

What can we say? This surpasses anything ever achieved by the BJ gang at lunch-time . . . we take our hats (and napkins) off to the Arabs!

EGGED ON . . .

Here's an interesting fact which will impress people and win you countless new friends when told at social gatherings. The greatest height from which fresh eggs have been dropped to earth without breaking is 198 metres (that's 650 feet). This feat was achieved in 1979 on Tokyo Golf Course by David Donoghue, who took his eggs up in a helicopter. No, we don't know why he bothered either . . .

YUM YUM . . .

Here are some tasty food facts to get your mouth a-watering.

The longest banana split ever made was *1.6 miles* in length and consisted of 15,912 bananas, 4319 litres of ice cream, 919 lb. of chocolate syrup, 1353 litres of cream topping, 276 lb. of nuts and 8910 cherries. It was made by the junior class of a New Jersey high school in 1983. What a feast!

The largest barbecue ever held was in Hawaii in 1981. There were 15,000 people in attendance and they managed to wolf their way through 46,386 half chickens. Phew!

The biggest apple pie ever baked was one made in 1982 over a period of three days in Kent. Included in the ingredients were 600 baskets of apples and enough pastry to bring the pie's weight up to 30,115 lb. Sloo!

The tallest wedding cake ever created stood at over forty tiers and had a height of 38 feet. It was made in Canada in 1983.

The largest ice cream sundae ever put together weighed 27,102 lb. and was full of strawberries, nuts and whipped cream when constructed in 1983 in Vermont. Sigh . . . true delight.

TOP OF THE CHOCS!

15

The best thing ever invented in the whole world must surely be chocolate. Derived from the cacao tree, it is thought to have originated in the Amazon basin where it was used as a type of currency. This was in 600 AD and the old bean has come a long way since then. Every year, millions of pounds are spent on this gorgeous creation and the biggest-selling chocolate in Britain is Kit-Kat. Tales that chocolate is a) fattening b) bad for the teeth and c) bad for the complexion are a) reasonably true b) not proven and c) without substantial evidence, so relax and eat chocolate to your heart's content — we love it!

WE ARE WHAT WE EAT . . .

. . . or are we? Well, we think this saying is basically false because if there was even a grain of truth in it, the staff of this office would closely resemble a dozen Mars Bars. And even worse, imagine what Monsieur Mangetout would look like . . . M. Mangetout (real name Michel Lotito) is a Frenchman who has been eating metal and glass since he was a nine-year-old boy. (This says a lot for his mother's cooking.) Experts who have X-rayed his stomach say that M. Mangetout's ability to consume 2 lb. of metal a day is "unique". (Plain loopy would be a better description.) This wacky Frenchman's diet has also included ten bicycles, a supermarket trolley, seven TV sets, six chandeliers and a yummy Cessna light aircraft. But to top it all, he has done the opposite of what most humans usually do and ended up with — ahem — a coffin (handles and all) inside his body. Weird, or what?

THE BJ QUICK AND EASY CALORIE-COUNTER

Nobody likes to count calories, so we just picked a few of the most crucial foods with their calorific values and listed them below . . .

ONE SMALL BAR OF CHOCOLATE . . . 300 CALORIES
ONE SLICE OF CHEESECAKE . . . 350 CALORIES
ONE ICE CREAM SUNDAE . . . 400 CALORIES
ONE SMALL ECLAIR . . . 250 CALORIES
THREE SMALL BISCUITS . . . 150 CALORIES

Em . . . as we said, nobody likes to count calories . . .

HUNK NO. 1:

MORTEN HARKET

As requested by:

Louise Dunton, Chesham.
H. Robinson, Norfolk.
Shona Baird, Inverness.
Louise Walklin, Essex.
Juliette Hambly, Jersey.
M. McCutheon, Co. Tyrone.
Barbara Beattie, Inverness.
Jenny Ross, Inkberrow.
Debbie Bowler, Aberdeen.

Tracey Dove, Jacksdale.
Natalie Player, Surrey.
Marie Anderson, Gwynedd.
Helen Chapman, Northampton.
Julie Williams, Swansea.
Jane Eagles, Andover.
Shona Anderson, Rotherham.
Marie Barry, Co. Cork.
Eve McKay, Kent.
Anne Povey, Kent.
Vicky Manning, Dursley.

Jacket, *from Clockhouse at C&A.*

Stripey gloves, *from Top Shop*

Rugby top, *by Staggers*

18

SIMPLY

IT'S HOT STUFF —

Cardboard briefcase,
*by Lifestyle
at House of Fraser*

Make-up case, *from BHS*

Tights and socks, *by Sunarama*

Boots, *model's own*

Lacy scarf, *from Salisbury's*

Umbrella,
from Top Shop

Patterned scarf,
by Pink Soda

Muff, from C&A

Wooden "Pencil" pencil box, from John Menzies

Hat, from Marks and Spencer

Teapot, from Habitat

Monopoly, from good toy shops

MONOPOLY

PROPERTY TRADING BOARD GAME

Waddingtons

red
ARE YOU RED-DY?

Spotty leggings and top, from Great Universal Stores catalogue

Lace up suede shoes, by Faith

Sweatshirt, from BHS

Rucksack, from BHS

Gloves and socks, from Top Shop

Stereo, by Sanyo

20

Scarf, from antique shop

Dress, by Via Satellite

Shoes, from Faith

Jumper and skirt, from Top Shop

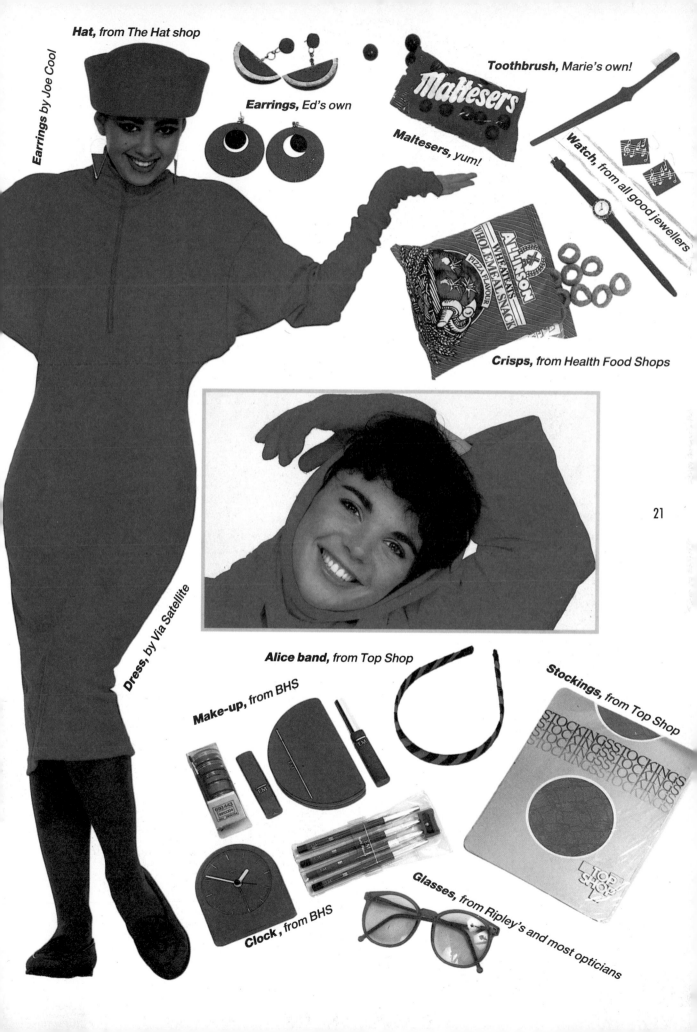

Hat, from The Hat shop

Earrings by Joe Cool

Earrings, Ed's own

Earrings, Ed's own

Toothbrush, Marie's own!

Maltesers, yum!

Watch, from all good jewellers

Crisps, from Health Food Shops

Dress, by Via Satellite

21

Alice band, from Top Shop

Make-up, from BHS

Stockings, from Top Shop

Clock , from BHS

Glasses, from Ripley's and most opticians

THE SECRET

The only person I could tell about Barry was a complete stranger I met in the park . . .

A GIRL with a Garfield carrier bag came and plonked herself on the park bench next to me. I moved along a little, to give her more room, and gave her a watery, preoccupied smile. Then I glanced at my watch and looked once again at the park gates, through the shivering trees, at the other end of the park.

"Waiting, are you?" The girl smiled, unpacked a polythene lunch-box, and poured herself a coffee from the thermos flask she had in the bag.

"Er . . . w-well . . . " I stammered.

"It's obvious, isn't it? You're sitting right on the edge of this bench, as if you're ready for take-off. And your nose is red, so you must've been here some time," she explained. She sipped her coffee, and looked at me over the rim of the cup.

I glanced at my watch again.

"Half an hour almost," I told her.

"They're always the same, aren't they? Never on time. Then they turn up with some pathetic excuse and before you know it, you've swallowed it whole! Fancy a coffee? Here — you

look as if you need it!" the girl said, pouring coffee into the top of the flask for me.

"Thanks." I shivered, accepting it gratefully. I held the cup in my hands, hoping that its warmth would do something for my frozen fingers. A bitter wind swirled round our ankles, and the carrier bag made a fluttering sound, like birds' wings.

"How did you know I was waiting for my boyfriend?" I asked. The warmth was making my brain work again. I had to be careful. I'd got into the habit of being careful over the weeks. I didn't want to let my guard slip now.

"So who else would be worth waiting for, on a park bench, on a day like this, eh?" She laughed. "Been going out with him long?"

"Six weeks," I said, without thinking.

"That all? You haven't even started yet! Let me tell you, the worst's yet to come! After six months, you'll be even colder, and even more fed up with the waiting, but you'll go on doing it. I just hope he's worth it."

I SHRUGGED, and blushed. The blush embarrassed me. I thought I'd learned over the last six weeks to be hard. I thought I'd learned to be secretive. Blushing showed that I hadn't learned as well as I thought.

"He's worth it," I whispered, glancing at the gate again. He was, wasn't he? Of course, he had his moods. And then, of course, there was the big problem that he wasn't quite mine, yet. There was Sarah, his girlfriend, the one he was going to finish with, any day now. Then we could stop all this — the waiting, the snatched meetings, the hurried, secret kisses. It would be a relief when it was all over. But he was worth it.

"Aren't they all!" The girl grinned. "Take mine, for instance. I tell you, I've had some trouble keeping him in line. Mind you, he's a nice-looking boy, and I'm not exactly an oil-painting myself, if you see what I mean . . ."

She looked all right to me. Ordinary — a bit like me, in a way. Medium-sized, medium height, with that funny mud-coloured hair that people call

23

mousey, just like mine. Hers was tucked under a bright mustard beret, and she had a mustard-coloured scarf to match, wrapped round her neck. She looked all right. And she smiled a lot, which is more than I'd been doing for a while.

ANYWAY, like I was saying, if you're nothing particularly special, and you think you've found a special boy, you have to put yourself out to keep him, don't you? Finished that coffee? I'd offer you another, only there's no more left . . . Going back to what I was saying, I reckon your bloke must be a bit like mine. Tall, dark and edible, right?"

"Right!" I agreed. I handed over my cup, and glanced at the gate again, then at my watch. "Tall, dark, edible, and three-quarters of an hour late! I have to get back to the shop in five minutes' time, too," I grumbled.

"The shop?" she asked.

"Morris'. The hardware shop round the back of the bus station. That's where I work — on the motor

accessories till."

"Oh yes! Let me guess . . . He was doing up an old banger, and came round to your shop for all the bits and pieces, eh?" she asked.

"Right. That's how we met. And then we started seeing each other, in the lunch-times, and sometimes after work, and . . ."

I stopped myself, mid-sentence. I'd already said too much. Barry had warned me not to say anything to anyone, not until he could see his way clear to finishing with Sarah, and I hadn't mentioned him to a soul, not even to my mate, Kirstin.

But when you keep something to yourself for so long, there's this feeling bubbling underneath, all the time, and you feel you've got to say something, or you'll burst. Talking to a stranger, a cheerful stranger in a mustard beret who was packing her lunch things back into her Garfield carrier bag, was the safety valve I needed. Especially after I'd been frozen to death on a park bench for almost the whole of my lunch-break.

I gulped and swallowed, and

looked down at my tight, cold fingers in my fingerless gloves.

"He's not coming," I whispered, almost to myself. A warm tear trickled down my cold cheek. "I've wasted another lunch-time. He's not coming. He didn't come yesterday, either."

The girl stood up, and sighed.

"Listen," she murmured, "I've got to get back to college. But if I were you, I'd forget about him. I'm sorry, whoever you are. But, like I said, keeping him's the hard thing to do. I'd do anything to keep mine. And when a mate mentioned that he'd been seen in the park, with this girl, at lunch-times, I had to move in, see? I got him into soccer practice at lunch-times. And I thought I'd just come and check you out, to let you know. He's special to me, too. I know he's not worth it, but I need him. Understand?"

I nodded, trying to sniff back the tears.

"'Bye, then," she said, swinging her scarf round her neck.

"'Bye, Sarah," I replied, watching her go, in her yellow beret, swinging that Garfield carrier bag, like sunshine on a bitter day.

Facing The
Earth

Clay-based face masks, like Mudd Mask, remove excess oils and unclog pores, help control spots and blackheads and make your skin softer and smoother.

Before applying the mask, soap your face with a hot, damp cloth and then dry gently. Leave the mask on for 10-15 minutes then gently wash it off with lukewarm water. (You may feel a slight tingling, but if your face starts to get at all sore, wash off the mask immediately.) These masks should only be used once a week on normal skins, and twice a week on very oily complexions.

If your skin's dry, clay masks will only make the condition worse — look for a good, moisturising one instead.

24

Elements
Water

● *Drink at least five glasses of water every day for a clear complexion and bright eyes.*
● *After you've rinsed the shampoo out of your hair with warm water, give it a final rinse under the cold tap. It'll make your hair look really shiny.*
● *If you're feeling all hot and bothered, hold your wrists under cool water for a few minutes.*
● *Water is one of the best skin toners there is — and it couldn't be cheaper!*
● *A very light spray of water will "fix" your make-up and make it last all day. Don't overdo it, though, or you'll end up with mascara and eye-liner running down your cheeks.*

Facing The
Fire

A fiery make-up suits just about every colouring and you can be as daring with it as you like.
Stick to golds and yellows as the basic eye-colours, using darker shades, like coral or even deep pink, at the outer corners, for added emphasis. Line your eyes with a smokey grey or dusky blue pencil, and finish off with two coats of dark grey, brown/black or gold mascara. (If you're very fair, light mascara could make your lashes disappear altogether, so you'd be best with one of the darker colours.)

Your lipstick should balance the look, so if you've been fairly subtle with your eyes, apply a gold, coral or orange lipstick — whichever tones best with the rest of your make-up. But if your eyes are fairly strong, a bright, bold red will complete the look perfectly.

Elements
Air

Too much heat can seriously damage your hair, so always keep your dryer on its coolest setting and hold it about nine inches from your head, moving it over your hair all the time so that the heat isn't concentrated on any one area for too long.

If you have to blow-dry your hair into a particular style, work a little mousse through it before you begin. Then section your hair and start drying, working your way round from the back of your head to the front, drying only a small section at a time.

Hair and make-up: Valerie MacDonald.

EMILIO ESTEVEZ
AGE: 25

Son of the much-acclaimed actor, Martin Sheen, Emilio Estevez decided to go it alone when he began his film career and kept his own name. Whether or not this made any difference nobody can be sure, but Emilio has gone from strength to strength in the movie world and has yet to receive a bad review for any performance. As well as being a more than competent actor, he also now writes screenplays, one of his more famous efforts being 'That Was Then, This Is Now'. Emilio lives in Los Angeles and those in the know tend to agree that he is the most popular member amongst the other Brat-Packers.

28

FILMS: TEX, REPO MAN, THE BREAKFAST CLUB, ST ELMO'S FIRE and THAT WAS THEN, THIS IS NOW.

ANDREW McCARTHY
AGE: 25

Cutie-boy Andrew McCarthy grew up in New Jersey but moved to New York when the University there offered him a place on their drama course. One of four McCarthy brothers, he now lives alone in two small rooms in Greenwich village, where he enjoys playing pool and listening to the music of Bruce Springsteen. Andrew claims to be a bit of a shy boy and often falls in love with his leading ladies, although he tends to keep his private life private and rarely mentions the names of his girlfriends.

FILMS: CLASS, HEAVEN HELP US, CATHOLIC BOYS, ST.ELMO'S FIRE, PRETTY IN PINK and PERFECT TIMING.

MATT DILLON
AGE: 23

Spotted by a film director during auditions held in his school, Matt Dillon began his acting career at the tender age of fifteen when he was chosen to play the lead in 'Over The Edge'. A native New Yorker, Matt comes from a large Irish-American family and despite his hectic film schedule, remains very close to his parents, four brothers and one sister. He drives a Porsche 924 and receives more than seven thousand fan letters a week.

FILMS: OVER THE EDGE, LITTLE DARLINGS, MY BODYGUARD, LIAR'S MOON, TEX, THE OUTSIDERS, RUMBLEFISH, THE FLAMINGO KID, TARGET and REBEL.

SEAN and CHRISTOPHER PENN
AGES: 27 and 24

Two for the price of one! Brothers Sean and Christopher Penn are both actors but perhaps the older of the two is also the most famous. Sean hits headlines with his peformances on screen as well as off and sparks certainly flew when he married temperamental pop star, Madonna. However, he has proved that he has real dramatic ability by winning several major roles and carrying them off with ease. He has co-starred in films with his wife, his brother and his best pals, Timothy Hutton and Tom Cruise. Both the Penns are from Santa Monica in California and have another star in the making in younger brother, Matthew.

FILMS: Sean — TAPS, FAST TIMES AT RIDGEMOUNT HIGH, BAD BOYS, THE FALCON AND THE SNOWMAN, AT CLOSE RANGE, SHANGHAI SURPRISE and CRACKERS. Christopher — AT CLOSE RANGE.

RALPH MACCHIO
AGE: 26

With his baby-faced good looks, Ralph Macchio has found it easy to play parts much younger than his real age. Like so many other Brat-Packers, he got his big break in 'The Outsiders' where he had one of the lead roles. But it is surely through 'The Karate Kid' films that he has gained most fame. Ralph trained with a karate specialist and spent a lot of time working on detailed kicks and moves for his part as the likeable Danny and both these films are still hits on video. In his spare time, Ralph enjoys reading, playing hockey and tennis and going out with his friends. He keeps himself to himself and lives beside his family in New York, where he recently acted in a stage play with Robert De Niro.

FILMS: UP THE ACADEMY, THE OUTSIDERS, TEACHERS, THE KARATE KID, THE KARATE KID II and CROSSROADS.

LEADERS OF THE PACK

MICHAEL J. FOX
AGE: 26

Thank heavens for little boys! Michael J. Fox may only be 5 feet 4 inches high, but he's certainly a big favourite with film fans. He began his acting career in TV's 'Family Ties' but gained international fame when Steven Spielberg's 'Back To The Future' became a smash hit. Michael is Canadian but now lives in a Hollywood ranch house, complete with swimming pool and heated spa. His hobbies include going to movies, playing ice hockey and listening to music such as U2. Michael has secret ambitions to be a musician and plays a mean guitar.

FILMS: MIDNIGHT MADNESS, CLASS OF 1984, BACK TO THE FUTURE, TEENWOLF, (JUST AROUND THE CORNER TILL THE) LIGHT OF DAY and CAGNEY.

C. THOMAS HOWELL
AGE: 20

Anyone who makes their film début in one of the biggest box office successes ever must surely be a bit special — and C. Thomas Howell is just that. Playing one of the boys in 'E.T.' at age thirteen, he went on to portray much more mature, and often difficult, characters in later films. The son of a stuntman, Tommy always wanted to be a famous rodeo rider and he won several championships before he followed his dad into a career as a movie stuntman. Then his picture was spotted by Steven Spielberg, who signed him up for 'E.T.' and C. Thomas Howell became a heart-throb.

FILMS: E.T., THE OUTSIDERS, TANK, RED DAWN, GRANDVIEW USA, THE HITCHER, SECRET ADMIRER and SOUL MAN.

29

ROB LOWE
AGE: 23

Rob Lowe has all the essential qualities to make him a perfect Brat-Packer — looks, money and a home in sunny Los Angeles. He loves fast cars and other hobbies include watching baseball, collecting sunglasses and having an on-off relationship with actress Melissa Gilbert. For his part in 'St Elmo's Fire', Rob learned how to play the saxaphone, and to play the lead in 'Youngblood', he trained for five hours every day and eventually put on fifteen pounds in weight — all muscle.

FILMS: THE OUTSIDERS, CLASS, HOTEL NEW HAMPSHIRE, OXFORD BLUES, ST ELMO'S FIRE, YOUNGBLOOD, ABOUT LAST NIGHT and SQUARE DANCE.

TOM CRUISE
AGE: 25

Out of all the Brat-Packers, Tom Cruise is the one with the biggest money-making pull at cinema box offices. Leading roles in a string of successful movies guarantee him the pick of the scripts in future films. He comes from a family of four and remains very close to his three sisters, who are his best friends. Tom originally began training as a priest, but found he wasn't cut out for the strict life and so turned instead to acting. Very polite and often shy, Tom lives alone in New York and has dated several famous Hollywood actresses, including Cher and Rebecca De Mornay.

FILMS: ENDLESS LOVE, TAPS, LOSIN' IT, THE OUTSIDERS, ALL THE RIGHT MOVES, RISKY BUSINESS, LEGEND, TOP GUN, THE COLOR OF MONEY and BRIGHT LIGHTS, BIG CITY.

ALI ▲

"Well, here is the 'typical' me, apart from the fact that I forgot to include a pair of v. large earrings, which I never go without.

"The Chinese dress cost £1.50 from a second-hand shop, as did the cute bag. There're about 84 bracelets here, all solid silver, haw! haw! The Crimpers and megahold hairspray are for spikey locks, 'cos flat hair is sad!

"The plant represents my house which has mucho greenery all over it. As for the bananas and Twists — well they're yummy, and Diet Coke salves my conscience after eating too much!"

WASTES OF TIME

The BJ Gang reveal the contents of their wardrobes and their innermost secrets. (Well almost!)

MAURA

"My very favourite dress! I bought it in Miss Selfridge for my sister's 21st and haven't stopped wearing it since. I love old black and white films, so I included this video of 'Wuthering Heights'. Anything with Laurence Olivier in it's an automatic winner, as far as I'm concerned.

"The holiday brochures are here because my main hobbies are — thinking about holidays, booking holidays, worrying about how to pay for holidays, looking at pics of holidays . . . "

LITTLE KAREN ▼

"Since I spend most of my spare time playing music, I thought I'd bring along my mandolin and some of my music books. The mandolin was actually a present to my gran on her 18th birthday, so it's probably an antique by now (didn't mean it, Gran, honest!). When I'm not annoying the neighbours with loud twanging noises, I also play golf — badly — and eat lots of curries. Unfortunately, it was rather difficult to rustle up a curry specially for this shot! As you may notice — as far as clothes go — red's my favourite colour!"

30

MARLYN

"I selected my jeans because I like to be comfy and don't 'dress up' very often. I do like trinkets, though, as you see here. The mortar and pestle aren't for making potions, but for grinding garlic and spices for curries, 'cos I'm a greedy pig and just love a good Indian meal. I like cats (and all animals) — here's the camera for taking pics of them!"

ALLIE ◄

"The skirt, earrings, necklace and shoes were all bought in a rush one Saturday afternoon when I had my first date with my ex-boyfriend. Blue is about the only colour which doesn't make me look pale and ill — like Lofty.

"When I moved away from home, my gran gave me this photo of my mum and dad's wedding and I keep it on my dressing table. I borrowed (!!) the paisley patterned scarf from my dad — he bought it in 1954!"

LEZ ►

"This is my fave outfit, 'cos I want to be a cowboy. It's fairly typical of me, i.e. there's many a black cloth involved. The boots aren't my faves — I was too busy wearing my faves at the time!

"Hairspray is a vital necessity of my life and I couldn't go anywhere without it, and the Chanel No 5 is a favourite because it actually stays on for quite a while!

"I like all types of music, but having seen Bon Jovi live I love this album. I pretend I bought their 'Slippery When Wet' book for work purposes but I really just lust over piccies of Jon!"

31

KAREN ◄

"This pinafore was the first thing I'd made since failing miserably at sewing in my schooldays, so I'm quite proud of it. I think everything else is obvious — I always have fresh flowers in my flat (except when they wilt), I love sea shells, old tins, flat shoes, cats, Prince and peanut butter. The gold star is a pretty ornament, but it's also a salt cellar which travels with me wherever I go!"

CALUM ►

"Well, you'd have to be pretty dense not to understand this lot! All the gear is for my motorbike (oh, surely not, Calum! — rest of the BJ gang). The instruction manual for fixing the bike is the one covered in grubby fingerprints. The record is Springsteen's boxed set — apart from being difficult to listen to on the bike, it's brilliant."

WASTES OF TIME

ALASDAIRE ▶

"This old coat is probably my most treasured piece of clothing. I bought it in a v. trendy Glasgow boutique called Metro, a couple of years ago. Alas, as you can see it's getting a bit old now — the sleeves are frayed and there're a couple of buttons missing (sniff!) but I'm loth to part with it .

"I was given the umbrella by this funky chick I used to know. It's actually got Prince's Purple Rain logo on it. At first, I just thought it was an ornament, but to my delight when I tried it in the rain it actually worked as an umbrella. Yes, I do lead a dull life . . .

"Unfortunately my most prized possession, my Roland Juno 106 polyphonic, programmable synthesiser was a bit too impractical to include here so I've put the manual in instead. What can I say about this keyboard? It's been a very close friend of mine for about a year now. We've been through a lot together. We share those special moments together and . . . (I think we get the picture. — The Ed.)

MARIE ▼

"I love skilled football, expensive aftershave and Irish books. The Irish are the best story-tellers in the world and George Best proves this with his autobiography. I might be biased, though, because I think George was the greatest footballer ever. The photo is of Pat Nevin and Mo Johnston, two Scottish players. I've been in love with Pat Nevin for three years now — he's a genius and I'll be genuinely disappointed if I don't marry him eventually!! The camera and Walkman are essentials for everyday life and the red card, book and whistle are essentials for football matches — I'm a referee. I sound like a real football fanatic, don't I?! (Never, Marie! — The Ed.)

32

GAYLE ▲

"This is my Sloane Ranger outfit — 'smart but casual'! I bought the Gladstone bag at an antique fair for £20. The album's by my hero, Van Morrison (OK, so I'm an ageing hippy!) The books are about Turkey which is my favourite country and about vegetarian cooking which is my favourite food. The black, shiny thing is my trusty Filofax (trendy or what?) and the little tortoise-shell reading glasses help me to intimidate the BJ gang. They think I look like a psycho-killer when I wear them!"

"REDUNDANT?" said my friend, Jackie, in a shocked voice, as we walked to school.

"Yes!" I fumed. "Mum told me last night. It's just not fair! Why does it have to be *my* dad?"

"I'm sorry, Sharon," sympathised Jackie. "It's not much fun when something like that happens."

"You're telling me!" I moaned. "Some Christmas this is going to be — we'll be lucky if we get a cracker each!"

"Never mind, Sharon," she comforted me, "I've got some great news to cheer you up. Clare Bloomer's having a party next Saturday and we're both invited."

"And that's not all," grinned Jackie, giving me a nudge. "Guess who else is coming — Paul Bailey."

I felt my face go hot. I'd always fancied Paul Bailey. He was a year above me at school, but I often passed him in the corridor. I'd always been too shy to speak to him, but he smiled whenever our eyes met. I was sure he liked me too.

"Oh," I said, trying to hide my enthusiasm.

"Mind you," she added, "that Sarah Smith has got her beady eyes on him — and she's coming to the party too."

My heart sank. "Oh, well," I sighed gloomily, "I needn't bother going then. There's no way he'll notice me if she's around. Her parents are so loaded she can afford a new outfit every time she goes out. I might as well wear a sack!"

"Don't be daft, Sharon!" scolded Jackie. "You can borrow some of my clothes if you like."

"No thanks," I replied stubbornly. "I want to wear my own clothes, or I'm not going."

"But you must," argued Jackie. "Can't you ask your mum and dad for some Christmas money in advance?"

"With Dad redundant? You must be joking!" I answered. "They made it pretty clear there'd be no expensive presents this Christmas."

The next few days were terrible. I couldn't get Paul out of my mind. Going to the party would be a great chance to get to know him, but what chance had I got against snobby Sarah?

Then suddenly, I had this brilliant idea. I'd buy some clothes myself — out of Jackie's mail order catalogue! Her mum ran an agency. I could pay each week out of my pocket money. I rushed round to Jackie's to tell her.

"But, Sharon," she warned. "My mum shouldn't really order anything without your parents' permission. If you can't pay they'll be responsible."

"Of course I can pay!" I told her, seeing myself impressing everyone at the party — especially Paul. "Oh, go on, Jackie. Just tell your mum that my parents are getting them for my Christmas. No one need know."

Jackie finally agreed and my clothes arrived a week later. I tried them on at her house then hid them in the bottom of my wardrobe so Mum wouldn't find them.

I COULDN'T wait for the party.

Jackie and I arrived early, but Sarah was already there, in a stunning pink satin-look blouse and matching trousers. She gave me an icy stare, jealousy written all over her face.

"I see you've been to the jumble sale again!" she jeered.

But I didn't take any notice, because I knew I looked every bit as good as her — if not better.

I looked round for Paul, but he wasn't there. I hoped he was going to turn up after all this! But I

needn't have worried. Jackie and I just had time to dance to a couple of records when in came Paul. My stomach turned somersaults as I watched him glance round the room. Then slowly his eyes came to rest on me.

"Would you like to dance?" he asked shyly, as he came across to our corner of the room.

I was stunned. The moment I'd spent months dreaming about had finally arrived.

The evening flew by as Paul and I danced and chatted together, and as everyone began to drift home, we arranged to meet the following evening.

"You know, I've always fancied you, Sharon," he confessed the next night as we walked through the park. "I should have asked you out earlier."

"Well, we can soon make up for lost time," I laughed.

"What! Three whole terms!" he joked back. "That'll take some doing."

Over the next few weeks, Paul and I saw each other whenever we could. It should have been the happiest time of my life, but there was one black cloud hanging over me — my new clothes.

I managed to scrape together the first two payments from my pocket money and a bit of my savings, but then it got more difficult. I only got £1.50 a week and I had things to buy for school out of that.

I tried and tried to get a Saturday job. I tramped round town for hours, but the answer was always no. I even tried for a paper round, but no luck there either.

"You owe me three weeks' money, Sharon," Jackie demanded one day.

"I know," I answered, biting my lip and wondering what to say.

"Mum's been asking for it," she fumed. "I'll cop it if she finds out the truth!"

"I'll pay you soon," I promised, wondering just how.

She glared at me, as though she knew I was lying. I felt really bad for letting her down. But what could I do? Dad would never give me a rise. He had carpets and things to pay for. Besides, he'd be furious if he found out what I'd done.

But I couldn't face telling Jackie that I'd deliberately deceived her, and even if I did, that wasn't going to help matters. *She* couldn't pay off my debts. Only Mum and Dad could do that and I wasn't about to tell them!

AS I came in from school that afternoon, I was miserable. How on earth was I going to get out of the mess I was in? Then I saw it — Mum's purse lying on the kitchen table. It was so tempting to take some money. But I'd never stolen anything in my life, especially from my own mum. I hated myself for even thinking of such a thing — but I could see no other way out. I took two pounds and hid it under my pillow. I'd give it to Jackie tomorrow.

I was no thief, though, and my guilty conscience plagued me all evening. "You've been talkative tonight," Paul joked as he walked me home from the disco. "I could hardly get a word in edgeways!"

I managed a smile. "I'm sorry, Paul. I didn't mean to be so quiet."

"I'm beginning to think it's me," he said. "You've not gone off me, have you?"

"Oh no, Paul! It's not that!" I answered quickly, hurt that he could think such a thing.

"Come on. You can tell me." He smiled. "Something's bothering you. I know."

He gave me such a kind look as he put his arm round me, I knew I couldn't keep it to myself any longer. I had to tell someone, and Paul looked so sympathetic. I was sure he'd understand.

"Oh, Paul," I cried, "I've just stolen some money from my mum. And I owe my friend, Jackie, about four weeks' pocket money . . . "

Then I explained the whole story to him — about the party and the clothes, and how I'd done it for him.

"Oh, Sharon," said Paul, wiping away the tears from my cheek. "I wouldn't have minded what you'd worn. You're still the same person underneath."

"Thanks, Paul," I whispered, giving him a kiss. It was the nicest thing he could have said.

"You'll have to tell your mum and dad what's happened," he said, seriously. "It's the only thing you can do. I'll come with you if you like."

"Would you, Paul?" I cried in relief. "That'd be great!"

MUM and Dad took it much better than I expected. They didn't shout at all, and Mum was really understanding.

"Why didn't you ask for some clothes?" she said anxiously. "We would have let you have some, especially for Christmas."

"Of course we would, Sharon," agreed Dad. "When we said we'd have to cut back this Christmas we didn't mean no presents at all."

He gave me a hug. "Cheer up, love. We'll help you pay off your debts this time, but you must promise never to go behind our backs like this again."

"I promise, Dad," I said softly, relieved it was all over.

Christmas was turning out much better than I'd expected, I reflected later. Who cared about expensive presents? I had something much better instead. I had Paul, a boyfriend who'd shown he really cared for me.

THE END

33

READER'S TRUE EXPERIENCE

A CHRISTMAS Wish

Normally Christmas is something you look forward to. But not this year. Not when your dad's just been made redundant and someone else has got their eye on the boy you fancy.

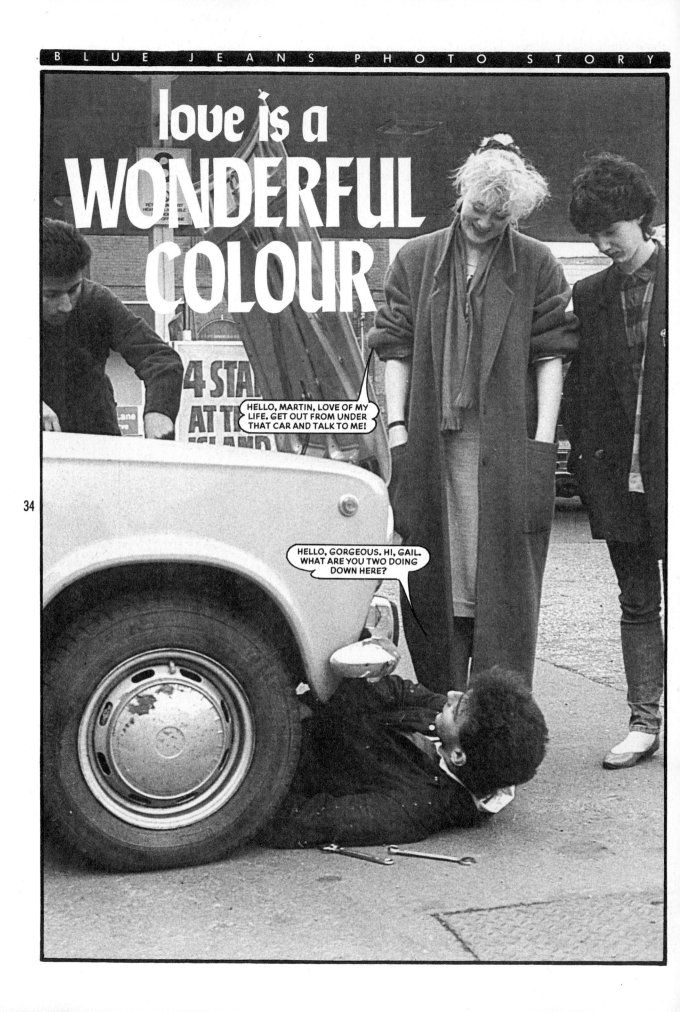

35

38

THE END

THE WEIRD AND WACKY
HISTORY OF HAIR

You just wouldn't believe the pains us women have had to go through over the years to have a hairstyle that's a little bit different...

1. This Bonnie and Clyde hairstyle was really outrageous when it was introduced in the twenties, and no doubt many a Mum had rows with her daughter when the traditional flowing locks got the chop!

2. Some younger American girls in the sixties whose pocket money didn't enable them to have their hair done professionally took pretty silly risks like this by ironing their hair so it hung straight and stiff. No doubt some of them had frazzled ears as well as hair!

3. This beehive hairdo is typical of the zany look created in the 1960's. It took hours of back-combing and gallons of hairspray to keep this style for any length of time. Some girls used to leave it for weeks before washing it! Yeeugh!

4. This looks like a kind of back-to-front Bo Derek style! The hair is rolled in small strands and brought to the front of the head. Only for the very brave!

5. The seventies heralded an era when girls started to try out any hairstyle which had been thought up — this girl looks as if she's a relative of Dr Spock!

6. Can you imagine turning up at your local disco looking like this? We hair experts at BJ reckon this Star Wars style is just ideal if you want to hide all those spots on your forehead and nose!

7. How many girls other than Bo Derek suit this style? It takes hours of a hairdresser's time (and lots of your money) to separate the hair into little plaits with beads.

8. Girls used to take hours over this sort of hairdo in the 1960's when they were getting ready for a night out. The brooch worn in the hair must have been pretty painful too!

9. Wow! This gal must have had to crawl from her front door on her hands and knees to keep her hair in place! The hair is gelled to a cardboard cone and topped with feathers.

10. With this style, it's very important to put your make-up on BEFORE you do your hair — how would you get at your face otherwise? It's decorated with feathers and pipe-cleaners!

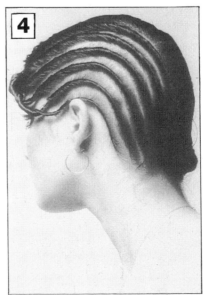

40

What Becomes Of The Broken-Hearted?

Rat! Creep! Pig! You've called him every name under the sun (and worse!) and you still don't feel any better. Try reading this feature, then. We can't patch up a broken romance, but we *can* make you feel more cheerful.

IF you've been arguing and fighting for the past few weeks, it often comes as a relief when one of you ends a relationship. But if things have been going smoothly (or so you thought!), being told "it's over" can come as quite a shock.

Of course, the longer you've known each other, the more it'll hurt, especially if you were one of those couples who did everything together. Your life will feel empty and yes, clichéd old phrase though it is, it can seem like the end of the world.

At this stage, crying is a pretty natural thing to do. Don't be embarrassed about this. It's far better to let your feelings out than keep them bottled up and gradually become bitter and resentful, not just towards your ex-boyfriend, but often towards everyone else as well.

Sympathy from friends, though, may seem to get a little overwhelming. A common reaction is: "I'm alone in the world. No one understands me." But don't brush your friends aside. They do genuinely want to help, and by confiding in them you'll take a great weight off your mind.

After you've got over the initial shock of the break up, it still takes time to get back to your normal, cheery self. We've drawn up a list of dos and don'ts to help you on your way.

Don't spend all your time alone in your room, playing records that remind you of your ex-boyfriend, staring at his photo and thinking about all the good times you had together. This will only make you more depressed and won't help you get over him. We're not saying that you should forget about your 'ex' completely, but now is not the time for reminiscing. Save that for six months', or a year's time when bringing back these memories makes you happy rather than sad.

Do get out and about. Go to parties and discos, join in school activities, get your friends together and arrange to go swimming, skating or shopping.

But what if you've been neglecting your friends since you met your boyfriend? Well, don't feel too guilty about it. It's a pretty common thing to do, especially at the start of a relationship. Ring your friends up, apologising for having ignored them, and suggest you meet up. It's highly unlikely they'll tell you to get lost!

Don't try to wriggle out of those parties, etc. by saying that you might meet your 'ex' there. So what if you do? Seeing him may bring back painful memories, but it's far more painful to confine yourself to the house just in case you happen to bump into him. Life must go on. You can't let one person turn you into a lonely,

miserable hermit.

Don't blame yourself because the relationship broke up. So the two of you didn't get along together, but that's not anyone's fault. You can't blame someone for being what they are any more than you can blame them for having blonde hair. Sitting there thinking "he'd still love me if I was thinner/prettier/more interesting" is a pointless exercise which will merely undermine your self-confidence. If he couldn't love you the way you are, then he's not going to love you just

because you lose 7 lb. or dye your hair red.

Do pamper yourself. Buy that record you've wanted for ages, or treat yourself to a new jersey or jewellery. You're going through a bad time at the moment, and there's no reason to make yourself any more miserable by denying yourself a few pleasures. A small treat now and then will give your spirits a lift.

Don't go running after him and beg him to take you back.

It's embarrassing for him and extremely humiliating for you. Every week, our postbag is full of letters asking "how can I get him back?". The simple answer is you can't. Your boyfriend obviously had his reasons for ending things, and no amount of persuasion on your part is going to change matters. By holding out false hopes that you can get back together, you are only prolonging your own agony. You must face the fact that the relationship is over.

Do be positive and look to the future rather than the past.

There are plenty more boys in the world. Ones that you won't like as much as your previous boyfriend and, yes believe it or not, ones that you'll like more than him. Of course, there's a lot more to life than boys, and just because you've got a boyfriend on your arm doesn't mean you'll be happy. Concentrate on enjoying yourself with your friends and forget about boys for just now. You deserve a break from the ups and downs of romance.

GOOD BOYS...

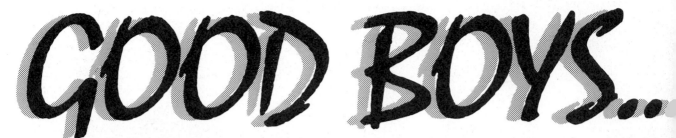

The nicey nicey boys of pop and film that even your mum fancies . . .

So they might be known as the Brat Pack, but not all the hunky young Americans involved in this hallowed group are nasty, horrible specimens of manhood. Tom Cruise, for one, is a positive charmer of a lad. How do we know that? Well . . . em . . . we just do, right . . . !

He's maybe had a few ups and downs in the past year or so, but underneath it all, Paul Young's a real toff . . .

Long brown hair, brown eyes, Sicilian good looks, wit, charm . . . what more could you ask for? Nino Firetto is a 'clean' boy if ever there was.

From the Levi boy who took his trousers off on TV to a top singing star, Nick Kamen has been a goody-two-shoes all the time. Whether you think he's an impressive singer or just a good-looking lad, we bet most of you are still lusting over him!

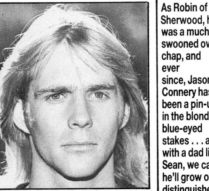

As Robin of Sherwood, he was a much swooned over chap, and ever since, Jason Connery has been a pin-up in the blond, blue-eyed stakes . . . and with a dad like old Sean, we can all hope he'll grow old and distinguished like him.

44

A-Ha . . . What else can we say? They don't drink, don't smoke, they wear jerseys their mums knit for them and the wackiest thing they do is have trendy three day stubble on their chins . . . rawwck 'n' rolll!

Jon Bon Jovi might be a bit of a dodgy-looking character, but we're assured he's a cutesie boy underneath that raucous rockin' exterior. Any rocker who bleaches the tips of his hair white is a true goody in our book.

Curiosity Killed The Cat are four trendy young Londoners, whose 'good boy' clean image is the kind your mum loves — and no doubt you're pretty keen on these boys, too . . .

Phew! Warrascorcher . . . Rob Lowe, whether he's cool and casual, or done up in his little tuxedo, he's a man indeed. That chin, that hair, that body . . . and he's a well-mannered lad to boot.

Michael J. Fox is actually twenty-four, but the parts he plays usually give him an average age of about sixteen . . . and that's much more believable. This chap's a big hit with youngsters everywhere and with his cutey-boy good looks and floppy little locks it's hardly surprising.

Bringing a whole new meaning to the term 'heavy metal' is Europe, that bunch of spankingly clean young Swedish funsters. Hair positively clean, outfits positively designer styled and faces positively babyish . . . whatever happened to ripped jeans, dirty leather biking jackets and matted hair, boys?

How could anyone resist those beautiful brown eyes? We certainly couldn't, and neither, we bet, can you. Nick Berry . . . a gem of a man, yes indeedy!

Whilst his ex-partner, Andy "how many cars have I smashed?" Ridgeley was being thrown out of night-clubs, smashing up cars and generally living the life of a rawck 'n' roll hero, George Michael was the complete opposite — quiet, well-behaved and positively saint-like . . . no skeletons in this lad's cupboard.

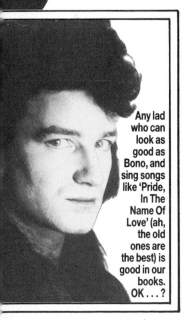

Any lad who can look as good as Bono, and sing songs like 'Pride, In The Name Of Love' (ah, the old ones are the best) is good in our books. OK . . . ?

Five Star . . . now there's a squeaky clean band if ever there was, eh, pals? Never has the boy-next-door had so much appeal to gals, and Delroy, for 'tis he, is the perfect example of a lad who'd do anything to help you out.

Our v. fave raucous rocker, Dave Lee Roth. With those flowing locks, that body and that sexy pout, we'd rock with you any time, Dave.

John-boy's Public Image has calmed down a lot since them thar Punk-rockin' days of 1977, but still he manages to sneer along with the best of them — scaree!

46

Mickey Rourke — Bruce Willis is just a cheap imitation — this is the REAL thing!

This mean and moody bunch have had a trendee cult following since their feedback-filled sound burst upon the unsuspecting ears of the nation a few years back. The Jesus and Mary Chain — not lads we'd like to cross, that's for sure!

Sullen Sean — he's moody, he's arrogant and no one would deny the lad's got a bit of a temper, but he must have some charm — this is the man who managed to capture the heart of everyone's favourite saucy young vixtress, Madonna!

Iggy Pop — definitely a God Of Our Time. This man is a divine being sent from above, and, to be honest, I'm too overcome with emotion just looking at this picture to say anything constructive!

The Men In Black may be getting on a bit, but as long as the kissy-kissy J-J Burnel is part of The Stranglers, they're still a definite winner with us!

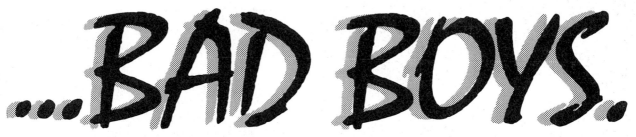

...BAD BOYS..

Why is it that bad boys always seem more fun than goody-goodies? We have a look at the best of the rawk 'n' roll rebels . . .

The Mission's Wayne Hussey — rawk 'n' roll was surely invented for this man . . .

Ooh, Zody — yummy yummy, what a honey! He tries hard to be a mean and moody mutha, but we know that underneath that filthy exterior, there's a Clean Boy just dying to get out.

Sigue Sigue's Martin Degville — oh, Marty babee, you tried too hard to be a Bad Boy — where art thou now?

The hero of many a goth up and down the country, Lux Interior of The Cramps is a mean dude if ever there was — and along with his chick, Poison Ivy, we're sure you'll agree they're an . . . er . . . interesting couple.

You either love him or loathe him, but you can't deny Prince is BAD! Think of it — he's small, skinny and not particularly fine-looking, but still he has many a female swooning. Yup — he's a Royal Rat, but we love him!

Ah, Sir William, what can we say that hasn't already been said at least 1000 times before? Those smouldering eyes! Those chiselled cheek-bones! Those luscious, pouting lips! That firm, tanned body! That smooth . . . (Cut! — The Ed).

LET'S HEAR IT FROM
THE

Just what does your average boy look for in a girl? Breathtaking good looks? A Swiss bank account? Samantha Fox's, em, musical talent? You'd be surprised. To find out, BJ cornered six unsuspecting males and grilled them as to just what it took to be their ideal woman . . .

DAVE
"I prefer quiet, sensitive girls actually. I'm not particularly keen on loud showy-off types. I'm a keep-fit fanatic, too, so I like reasonably sporty girls."

What sort of girls don't you like, then?

"Well, as I said, loud obnoxious females are a real pain and I loathe big, glamorous types with nothing between their ears."

And your ideal night out?

"Em, a quiet meal together, then maybe we'd go and watch a film."

JOE
"I like bright, cheery girls with a good sense of dress. By that I mean that they dress for the occasion. There's nothing worse than sitting in a greasy café somewhere and she's dressed to the nines, is there?"

What kind of female d'you not like then, Joe?

"Definitely not panicky girls who get hysterical at the least little thing. I prefer calm, level-headed girls. Oh, and I hate females with squeaky voices. That's a real turn-off!"

What about chat-up lines? Which ones do you use?

"Actually, I prefer when the girl takes the lead and starts talking to me first."

JOHN
"I like girls who're good-humoured and easy to get on with. Physically, I prefer blondes, particularly leggy blondes. I guess that's a bit predictable, though."

Mmm, just a bit. What sort of girls don't you like?

"Definitely girls who think a lot of themselves and wander round expecting everything in trousers to fancy them."

Chat-up lines?

"Em, can't think of anything at the moment. Usually it just occurs to me at the time."

Who's your ideal woman, then?

"Oh, it's a toss-up between Farrah Fawcett and Sarah Greene."

Sarah Greene . . . ?

"Yeah, Sarah Greene. I think she's dead sexy."

BOYS

KEITH

"My ideal girl? She'd have to have a sense of humour, be outgoing and she'd obviously have to be interested in the same things as me."

Such as?

"Well, she'd have to like David Bowie for a start, enjoy paaartying all night long and I must admit a healthy interest in football wouldn't go amiss either."

What would your perfect night out consist of?

"Definitely, a candlelit dinner for two and then we'd go down to the club and dance through to the morning."

ANDY

"My ideal girl wouldn't be the glamorous woman about town or anything. I'd far prefer someone down-to-earth who had similar interests to my own, such as music, reading and things. Physically, I like dark-haired girls with dark eyes."

What kind of girls don't you like?

"Hmm, definitely ones who come on really strong the first time you meet them. I actually prefer shy girls to really forward ones."

What's your favourite chat-up line?

"Again, I don't use them. They're so false. I like to get the vibes of the situation and then I just act accordingly. It always pays off . . . "

Yeah, maaan!!

PHIL

Describe your ideal girl, Phil?

"Well, I can sum up my perfect woman in one word."

Uh-huh, and what's this word, then?

"Jackie."

Jackie?

"Yeah, Jackie, that's my girlfriend.

"Anyway, to me, the essential things about a woman are good clothes, a car with plenty of room in the boot and she must have lots of money. Good clothes, so she looks good when we're out together and plenty of cash, so she can take me to trendy, expensive nightspots."

So what's so important about the boot capacity of her car?

"Oh, that. Well I play bass in a band, so obviously I need a girl who can cart my gear around!"

LET'S HEAR IT FROM
THE

Well, so much for the boys, here we give the girls a chance to tell us what makes their perfect man . . .

CATHERINE

"I like tall, dark-haired men with brown eyes. A crazy sense of humour like mine's also essential. Oh, and musical taste's important, too. It'd be dreadful if you were at a disco with this supposed ideal man, and he refused to dance to any of the things you liked."

What sort of boys don't you like?

"Definitely the ones who ignore you for a whole night at a disco, and then as soon as the last record, the slow smoochy one, gets played, they're all over you. Yeugh!"

Corniest chat-up line?

"Well, the worst one I've heard is surely, 'Is there enough room in your handbag for the keys to my Porsche?'"

LORRAINE

"I know it's predictable, but a sense of humour really is top priority with me. I don't like over-confident blokes and I don't like guys who're too shy — somewhere between the two would be perfect."

What do you dislike?

"Loud show-offs just don't interest me and I loathe smoking."

What's the worst chat-up line you've heard?

"What was it again? Em, 'You've got a smile like a ton of Colgate!'"

And the best one?

"Well, I think chat-up lines are dead false so there isn't really a best one. Conversation should just come naturally."

Ideal man?

"Paul Young — definitely."

JUNE

"Someone well-mannered, reasonable-looking with a sense of humour. Physically, I like tall, dark boys with brown eyes."

Dislikes?

"Em, dead serious blokes and guys not into disco-ing."

And your perfect night out?

"Ooh, a pizza somewhere and then on to a big disco."

Sounds vaguely familiar, June . . .

GIRLS

LESLEY

"My dream guy would be tall, dark and strong with a good sense of humour. I don't like guys who're deadly serious all the time but on the other hand I'd hate him to treat everything as one big joke. I'm not very keen on boys who rely too much on smart, trendy gear to impress the girls. Clothes don't make the man and all that."

And your idea of a perfect night out?

"Well, I'm afraid I'm one of the 'quiet night in' brigade, so I'd settle for an Indian takeaway and some soft, romantic music."

Worst chat-up line?

"Well, would you believe me, I've had the old 'D'you come here often?' routine pulled on me? That was probably the worst. No, I think a simple introduction and a guy asking you to dance is far better than any clever remark."

LINDA

"My Mr Perfect would be about 5' 8", dark-haired, with a dark complexion and a hairy chest! He'd have to be kind, like music and be reasonably stylish, clothes-wise."

What about personality then, Linda?

"Personality-wise, he'd be quite outgoing and ambitious. Reliable but still willing to take a chance."

What sort of guys don't you like?

"Em, I don't like boys who're too fat or too skinny and I loathe guys with messy hair. I also hate loudmouths."

So, can you name somebody who fits your picture of the perfect man?

"Oh, someone with the looks of Eddie Kidd and the talent of George Michael would do nicely!"

ELAINE

Describe your ideal boy.

"Well, someone tall and dark with classy dress-sense and short, neat hair wouldn't be far off the mark. He'd be great fun to be with but would have a sensitive side to his character."

What d'you dislike in a boy, then?

"Loud, boisterous guys are a real bore. In fact, if someone's acting like he's God's gift to women, there's nothing I like better than bringing him down a peg or two!"

Em quite. Who's your perfect man then?

"Mmm, Tom Cruise."

THE BB AWARDS

Cue fanfares, trumpets — it's that time of the year, again fun fans. Time for the world-famous and highly prestigious (eh?) Blue Jeans Awards. Who will win our coveted Golden Wispa trophies this year? The world waits with bated breath . . .

THIS YEAR'S BEEN A COMPLETE AND UTTER WASH-OUT AWARD

Poor Paul! His singles went absent without leave from the charts, the 'newspapers' had a go at him, his ex-girlfriend had at go at him, and now we're having a go at him. Except, we're not really. We still think he's a nice boy, so there. Don't let them get you down, Paul. Here, have some of our Kleenex.

MINERS CONTRIBUTION TO MAKE-UP AWARD

Who else but Deneice from 5 Star? This dudess must apply her eye make-up with a shovel. What are the pointy bits for, do tell us purlease!

NAUGHTY BOY OF THE YEAR AWARD

Oooh, it's slappy-wrists time for Jools (*!*!) Holland. We know 'The Tube' can be pretty dodgy at times — but there *are* other ways of taking a holiday.

Wash your mouth out with some Carbolic, boy!

FEMALE COMEBACK OF THE YEAR AWARD

Yes, it's the Princess of Peroxide herself, Ms Debbie Harry. Take a bow, Debs — it's great to have you back. That "French Kissing In The USA" single was quite a mouthful though, wasn't it?!

SUCCESS STORY OF THE YEAR AWARD

From denim breeks to pop mega-stardom, what more could a cheeky chappie ask for? Check out that smile, Nick Kamen seems pretty pleased with his lot, doesn't he?

MOST ANNOYING HUMAN BEING WHO EVER WALKED THIS EARTH AWARD

A joint award, this one — so we'll leave them to bite and scratch about who takes home the Golden Wispa. Come on down, Jonathan King and Samantha Fox — you're even more annoying than a game of Trivial Pursuit.

MOST UNATTRACTIVE BAND TO HAVE A HIT RECORD AWARD

The poor, ol' Housemartins win this category hands (or should it be face?) down!

Let's be honest, ver lads have features only a Mummy could love.

MOST ATTRACTIVE BAND TO HAVE A HIT SINGLE AWARD

Drool! Swoon! Step forward, Curiosity Killed The Cat. Four fine men, and true. Who's *your* favourite, favourite, gals? Answers on a postcard, please!

POP QUIZ

So you think you know everything from Stedman's shoe size to Cyndi Lauper's natural hair colour, do you? Find out the truth by trying your hand at this spiffy quiz . . . it'll sort out the men from the boys . . .

1. What's the real name of Dave Vanian, lead singer with The Damned?

2. What was the name of the first boppy hit by those dodgy Germans, Modern Talking, who was some kind of relative?

3. Golden oldie time! What was the name of T.Rex's first No. 1 and what year was it?

4. What was the name of the first chart-orientated band Vince Clark was in?

5. What is the name of Alison Moyet's little boy?

6. Where do Five Star hail from?

7. What was the name of Billy Idol's punk band whose biggest hit was "King Rocker" in 1979?

8. The Housemartins had a No. 1 at the end of '86 with "Caravan of Love" — who originally recorded it?

9. What advert did Nick Kamen start off his rise to fame in?

10. What was the name of the Brat Pack film that gave Berlin their first No. 1 with "Take My Breath Away"?

11. What jolly spiff job did Pet Shop Boy, Chris Lowe do before he discovered rock 'n' roll?

12. What is the name of Swing Out Sister's lead gal?

13. In which way are Mel and Kim related?

14. What old Abba song did Doctor and the Medics cover?

15. Which song did Debbie Harry make her comeback with at the end of last year?

16. Whose mother, in an exposé about her son, said he was "the ugliest baby she'd ever seen"?

17. What was the rather pretentious name of U2's album, released in March?

18. Which Glasgow band was originally a punk combo known as Johnny and the Self-Abusers?

19. Who else recorded the original version of "Don't Leave Me This Way" which was a No. 1 for The Communards?

20. What was Ben Volpeliere-Pierrot's job before turning into a mega-famous singing star?

21. Which v. romantic island do that massive singing family, The Jets, come from?

22. What was the completely over the top, outrageous title of Queen's first album?

23. What was the name of Mission singer, Wayne Hussey's previous band?

24. What was the name of the Icicle Works first chart hit?

25. What is the occupation of Jon Bon Jovi's dad?

26. How tall is Mags from A-Ha . . . is he a midget or a giant?

27. Who was the Scots songstress that Prince has teamed up with a couple of times to write some groovy toons?

28. Where did Spandau Ballet kick off their "Across The Borders" tour at the end of last year?

29. Name the two brothers in The Psychedelic Furs.

30. What was Madonna's first UK No. 1?

She's Got Legs...

SHOW A LEG

LEGS haven't always been on show, y'know. At the turn of the century, even a glimpse of shapely ankle in polite company was enough to get a gal banned from Lady Cynthia's tea and crumpets parties for ever.

In the 1910s, though, daring new fashions raised hems to mid-calf level — no doubt to the extreme disapproval of Lady Cynthia and her chums. Although skirts didn't get much shorter until the 1940s, at least you could show a leg in a bathing costume as they shrank to manageable proportions — it can't have been much fun trying to swim with seventeen yards of material covering every square inch of your body.

In the 1940s it was OK to show even a bit of knee (cor!) but at the same time, gals with knobbly knees started to cover up with trousers.

Things didn't change much length-wise until the 1960s when they got very silly indeed. Skirts got so short that they became little more than belts. Frostbite was a distinct possibility even in the middle of summer.

Modesty gained the upper hand briefly in the seventies as hemlines dropped and knees disappeared, but the wild and wacky eighties have thrown all conventions to the winds. Skirts can be long, short, narrow, wide anything a gal wants as long as it's worn with style. So no matter what you think are your legs' bad points, there's bound to be some way you can show them off!

FOXY vixtresses wanting shapely pins should boogie on down with these exercises.

1. **Stand on your toes with feet apart. Lower yourself into a crouch with your hands on the front of your thighs, knees outwards. Now straighten legs as you lower your heels. Repeat 9 times.**

2. **Kneel on the floor, back straight and arms held out in front at shoulder height. Bending only at the knees, lean back as far as possible without straining. Now return to vertical. Repeat 9 times.**

3. **Kneel on all fours with back straight. Bring left knee forward to touch chest then extend leg backwards straightening as you go. Repeat 9 times without touching the floor. Repeat with the other leg.**

Got that? Right, now go for the burn!

Most gals hate their legs. They're too fat, too thin, too knobbly, too short or whatever. But there's more to your legs than keeping your bum off the ground . . .

Chaka Khan cheers up chubby gals everywhere by showing that you don't need matchstick legs to get to the top.

Madonna — ever the classy dresser — shows that subtlety is always the best when it comes to legs.

LEGS ELEVEN

— Eleven very interesting facts about legs (honest!)

1. The creature with the most legs is a millipede called Illacrne Plenipes which is found in California USA. It has 375 pairs of legs — that's a total of 750.

2. The longest muscle in the body is the Sartorius which runs across the front of the thigh.

3. In 1942, Marlene Dietrich's legs were insured for £175,000, Fred Astaire's for £200,000 and Betty Grable's for a staggering £250,000.

4. Of 126 bones in the body, there are 31 in each leg.

5. The largest, heaviest bone in the body is the thigh bone (the femur if you want to be technical).

6. The knee is the largest joint in the body, the ankle the strongest.

7. The unluckiest legs in the world must belong to frogs. Highly prized by gourmets in France (where they'll eat anything), millions are raised every year just to have their pins scoffed (blech!).

8. Of athletes, basketball players and rowers have the longest legs, gymnasts and divers the shortest.

9. Legs are pretty hard-working. In a normal day, the average woman takes around 27,000 steps. (Most of these are to the canteen in the case of the BJ Gang, har, har.)

10. When dieting, legs are often the last part of the body to show any improvement, leading to the myth that legs don't respond to dieting.

11. Lego, the kiddie's building bricks, haven't got anything to do with legs, but I'm getting desperate. (OK, that's enough, I'm stopping this feature now! — The Ed.)

Sexy vixtress, Patsy Kensit, well known for showing a shapely limb.

Twiggy's legs were the envy of every gal in the sixties. Not much to envy . . .

Sizzling, soaraway S'manfa Fox shows why she's not famous for her legs.

Mark Hateley modelling the best pair of legs in football (except Pat Nevin's) according to Marie.

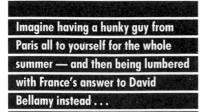

Imagine having a hunky guy from Paris all to yourself for the whole summer — and then being lumbered with France's answer to David Bellamy instead . . .

JEAN. PAUL

HEATHER

by Lorraine Forrest

Saturday

I can't believe it. This time tomorrow, he'll be here! After weeks of grovelling, keeping my room tidy and putting the top back on the toothpaste, Mum and Dad actually agreed to have a French student to stay with us during the summer hols — and he arrives tomorrow!

His name's Jean-Paul, he's sixteen and he comes from Paris. I bet he's got dark, sensuous eyes and olive skin — and the sexiest French accent ever! We'll probably fall hopelessly in love and he'll whisk me off to some chateau in the South of France.

My mate, Heather, is really peeved because her Dad doesn't like the French (something to do with rugby) and wouldn't even think about them having a student.

My idiot brother, Pete, rang from London this evening. (Reversed charges, as usual!) He's decided to give up trying to become an actor and is now thinking of going into politics. Dad's reply was unrepeatable — as usual.

Sunday

Heather turned up on the doorstep at five past seven this morning to ask if Jean-Paul had arrived yet. Even the milkman doesn't arrive that early!

The day really dragged — until Jean-Paul arrived at three-thirty , carrying one small overnight bag and a microscope. He can't be an inch over five foot, has pale blue eyes and mousy brown hair. As for the "sexy French accent", it's completely non-existent. Still, Heather thinks he's cute — but that could be because she's even smaller than he is!

"My dear friend, Deborah," he said, sounding like a cross between Maggie Thatcher and Prince Charles. "While I reside in your home I shall speak only in English. You must feel free to correct my grammar and pronunciation whenever necessary." He's got to be joking — he speaks English better than I do.

Pete rang again to ask if anyone knew David Owen's telephone number. Mum said, "Who's David Owen?"

Monday

Went on a nature ramble with Jean-Paul and Heather. He collected tons of mosses, wild flowers, slugs, worms, frog spawn and a dead sparrow — then he made us look at bits of each one under the microscope. It was disgusting.

"Isn't science wonderful, Deborah?" Jean-Paul said, dissecting a slug, as I tried not to throw up.

"Yes — it's absolutely fascinating," Heather piped up. "Did I tell you I want to study biology when I leave school?" (Funny, she's always telling me she wants to be a hairdresser.)

Mum spent half the night on the phone to Aunt Polly. She and Uncle Jim have fallen out yet again. I'm sure it'll blow over, though — it always does.

Tuesday

Saw a really boring play at the Arts Centre about socialism in the 15th century. Naturally, Heather and Jean-Paul thought it was "absolutely fascinating."

When it was finished, Jean-Paul suggested that we go for something to eat. "Great!" I said, beginning to think he was human after all. "McDonald's?"

"I had rather hoped to go to a health food restaurant where one could enjoy a soya and nut cutlet," said Jean-Paul.

"Oh, I know one," squeaked Heather looking really smug. I'm rapidly going off that girl.

To top it all, Jean-Paul wants to go

bird-watching tomorrow. I don't think I'll be able to survive another three weeks of France's answer to David Bellamy.

Wednesday

In bed all day suffering from food-poisoning. So much for health food! Jean-Paul's stomach is obviously used to digesting textured vegetable protein, because he was up at six and on his way to Blackthorn Heath by ten past. It was almost worth the suffering to get out of bird-watching!

"We've brought you a get well soon present, Debbie," Heather said, dumping a bunch of wild flowers on my bed later.

"Very nice." I couldn't help noticing loads of suspicious-looking black things on them.

"And I have brought you something very special!" Jean Paul added proudly. "A feather from the Lesser Spotted Double-Billed Blue Crest!"

Just what I've always wanted!

Mum was on the phone to Aunt Polly for hours again. It must be more serious than I thought.

Thursday

It is! Aunt Polly's moved in with us — she's brought the baby, the twins, Spot the dog and Joey the budgie. Dad said "This place is turning in to a hotel." (Actually he put it a bit more strongly than that!)

Mum's put a spare mattress in Jean-Paul's room for the twins, and she wants

56

FAIR EXC

DEBORAH

crazy if he'd caught a glimpse of Uncle Jim in the car. (Yes, he was still there!)

Heather, my so-called best friend, refused to come with us because Pete was going to call round later to teach her "vocal technique in alternative drama". She'd listen to the life story of Gregor the Grasshopper if she fancied the guy who was telling it!

Anyhow, we decided to go up to Blackthorn Pond, the idea being that the twins could collect frog spawn, the dog could sniff other dogs, Jean-Paul could study the natural habitat of the green frog and I could listen to my new 'A-Ha' tape on my Walkman in peace. Peace? Did I say peace?

The dog went berserk when it saw some stupid poodle and tore off after it, landed in the middle of the pond, got caught up in some fibrous vegetation (Jean-Paul's description) and disappeared!

The kids started howling their heads off, so Jean-Paul dived in to save him! Being a half-witted, dumb animal, Spot panicked, bit Jean-Paul's ear and pulled them both under!

"Somebody help them!" I screamed. "They're drowning!"

Just then, Jean-Paul surfaced, grabbed Spot by the collar and dragged him to the side. He looked dead cool (Jean-Paul, not the dog!) emerging from the water, covered in mud, with blood trickling down his neck. It was pretty impressive, I can tell you!

Suddenly, we seemed to be surrounded by mums and dads and kids and police and reporters. The kids leapt on the dog and started hugging and kissing him and everyone else cheered and whistled. Next thing I knew, I was in Jean-Paul's arms, laughing and crying and saying stupid things like "you could have been killed" and "I didn't know you were so brave".

Mum went hysterical when the police car pulled up at the door and four bedraggled figures and a dog got out. Aunt Polly and Uncle Jim were so relieved the twins were OK, they ran to each other, declaring undying love and forgiveness, and even Dad stopped moaning now that *his* lodger was a national hero. (Well, maybe not quite — but he *did* get his photo in the local paper.)

Jean-Paul said I should learn to speak French if I want to spend next summer at his chateau. He really has one! Can you believe it! I just melt when he says, "Le petit fleur est très joli." I never knew studying hedgerows could be so fascinating!

And y'know, I think living over here must suit him, 'cos he looks to me as if he's grown at least two inches taller since he arrived . . .

57

me to share my bed with Aunt Polly and the baby! I'd rather sleep on the floor!

Jean-Paul offered to sleep on the settee, but Mum wouldn't hear of it. He helped me draw up a rota this afternoon. It's a bit awkward only being allowed to visit the bathroom at certain times of the day, but the meal sittings seem to be working well!

The twins think the microscope's brilliant. I suppose it *was* pretty nice of Jean-Paul to let them play with it. He even cleaned out the budgie's cage and took the dog for a walk. I guess he's all right, really . . .

Pete rang yet again. He can't get hold of David Owen, so he's coming home tomorrow! He'll have to sleep in the bath!

Friday

Woke up with a sore back because the dog was lying on top of me. Uncle Jim turned up and begged Aunt Polly to come home. She said she'd never be able to forgive him, was happy living with us and wanted a divorce! Uncle Jim said he'd wait in the car.

Pete came home with six month's washing and a very large overdraft. He said that being an actor was his "true

vocation" and as soon as he was back on his feet he'd try again. Jean-Paul mentioned that his father was a film producer (Wow!) and he'd see what he could do for him!

Heather called round as soon as she heard that Pete was back. She's fancied him for years. She's incredibly fickle, that girl!

Borrowed a fiver from Dad and the four of us went to a disco. Jean-Paul didn't look quite so short in the dark and he's not a bad dancer, really.

Uncle Jim has been sitting in the car for fourteen hours.

Saturday

What a day! Talk about excitement!

It all started when Mum asked Jean-Paul and me to take the dog and the twins out for the day because Aunt Polly was heading for a nervous breakdown. I must admit, spending the day with a dalmation, two six-year-old kids and a natural scientist sounded pretty dull to me. How wrong can you be?

Off we set with the usual bottles of lemonade, bags of crisps and boxes of paper hankies. (Why do mothers always have an abundant supply of paper hankies?) We had to sneak out the back way, because the dog would've gone

HANGE...

Christmas time invariably means invites to many a party. Fun, fun, fun! Or so it should be, anyway. Follow our tips to make sure every party you go to is better than the last . . .

PARTY GAMES

A party is — 'a social gathering for pleasure, often held as a celebration'. So says the Collins English Dictionary, anyway, and who are we to argue? Sounds fairly harmless put like that, doesn't it? So why are parties often dreaded by many an otherwise sane personne?

'Tis a mystery, it surely is. As this is the traditional party season, you're bound to be invited to at least one. Or, if you're a truly wacky funster, you could well be throwing a bash of your own. The important thing to remember about any party is to enjoy yourself. It's no use moping around or sobbing your eyes out on the stairs over the love of your life who's decided to be the love of sexy Sue's life instead and has given you the chuck. For a start, your make-up will run and you'll be in the way of everyone trying to go up/down the stairs. Hardly makes for a fun-filled evening now, does it?

So, go only if you're in at least a half-way decent mood. Otherwise, unless something truly outstanding happens, you'll find that you're fairly bored, the music isn't your taste and the party funsters in general get on your nerves. Don't go and plonk yourself in a corner all evening either, with nothing but a few peanuts for company. The general idea behind parties is to circulate, meet people and generally be sociable. Even if you arrive and find that you don't know a soul, don't panic. There's an easy way to make small talk at parties. Turn round to the nearest person and say the first thing that comes into your head. Even if it's a load of old tosh about the wondrous festive weather, it's more interesting than nowt. And if the object of your wit and charm stares blankly/runs away/starts screaming, move on to someone else until you find someone who's just as wacky as you are. You'll soon be chatting away to one and all and you'll become known as the Life and Soul of the Party.

YOUR OWN PARTY

If you're being a brave soul and throwing a party of your own, it's important not to try too hard. After all, once the guests have arrived, the music is a-stompin' and the food and drink a-flowin', there's not really a lot you can do to help matters. No two parties are the same — you could throw a pair of them in the same week, invite the same people and play the same music and still they wouldn't be the same. You can't do much to control the atmosphere, so throw caution to the wind,

forget being cool and street-cred and concentrate on having a good time.

WHO TO INVITE

A mixed crowd of different types always works well. A party can either be a small, intimate gathering where most of the people know each other, or a riotous screamin' time where everyone jumps up and down, does a few handstands and the like — generally make fools of themselves, in fact. Personally, we go for the screamin' time. Don't invite pop stars or celebs — they probably won't turn up and if on the off-chance they do, they'll simply upstage you and everyone'll forget it's your party in the first place. Try to invite a more or less equal amount of both sexes — although no one admits to it, people quite like to pick up chicks/dudes at parties. A few wacky, extrovert personnes are good to have at parties to get things movin' — which is why the BJ gang are invited to so many social gatherings!

GOLDEN RULES OF PARTIES

DO talk to as many people as possible.

DO act as if you're having a good time i.e. smile and laugh a lot.

DO leave yourself time to get ready — you don't want to turn up feeling like a tinko.

DO wear something you feel comfy in — there's no point in wearing a saucy, slinky number if you feel so self-conscious you hide in the corner all night.

DO make sure there's lot of party music if it's your party. Your 'Greatest Lurve Songs' LP may be a winner, but it's hardly stompin' music.

DON'T stand in a corner giggling with a chum all night — hysterical girls don't make good impressions.

DON'T drink alcohol — drunken people always make fools of themselves and later regret it.

DON'T waste your time desperately looking for a young hunk to chat up. You'll have a much better time just chatting to everyone rather than eyeing up potential boyfriends all night.

DON'T stay out after the time your parents have told you to be in by. You'll only worry them and spoil things for the future.

DON'T walk home on your own.

There — fairly simple, isn't it? Have a great time now!

61

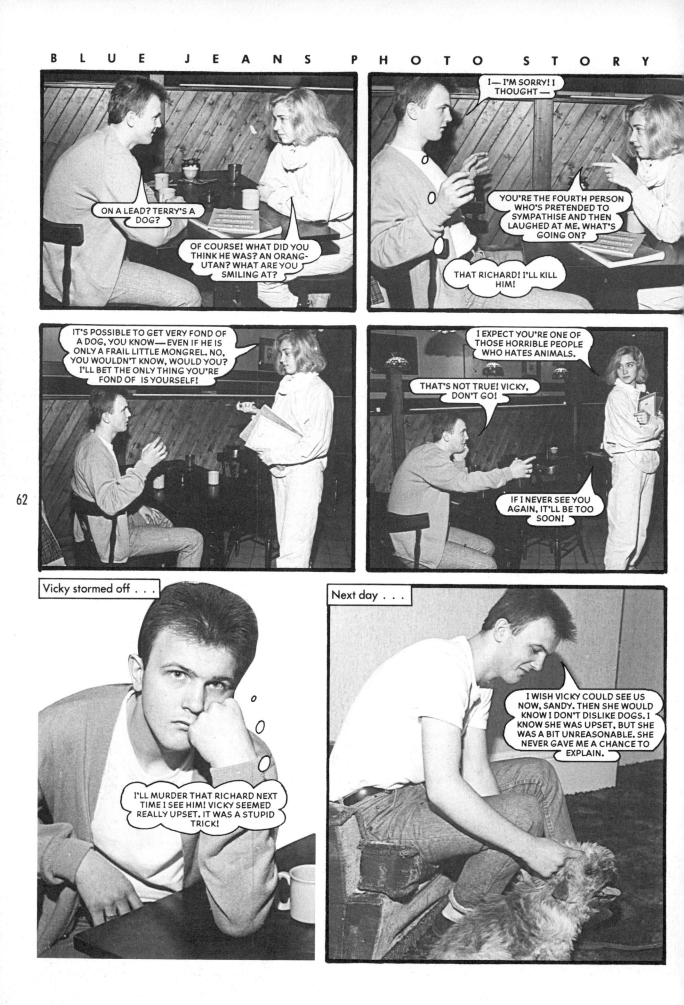

62

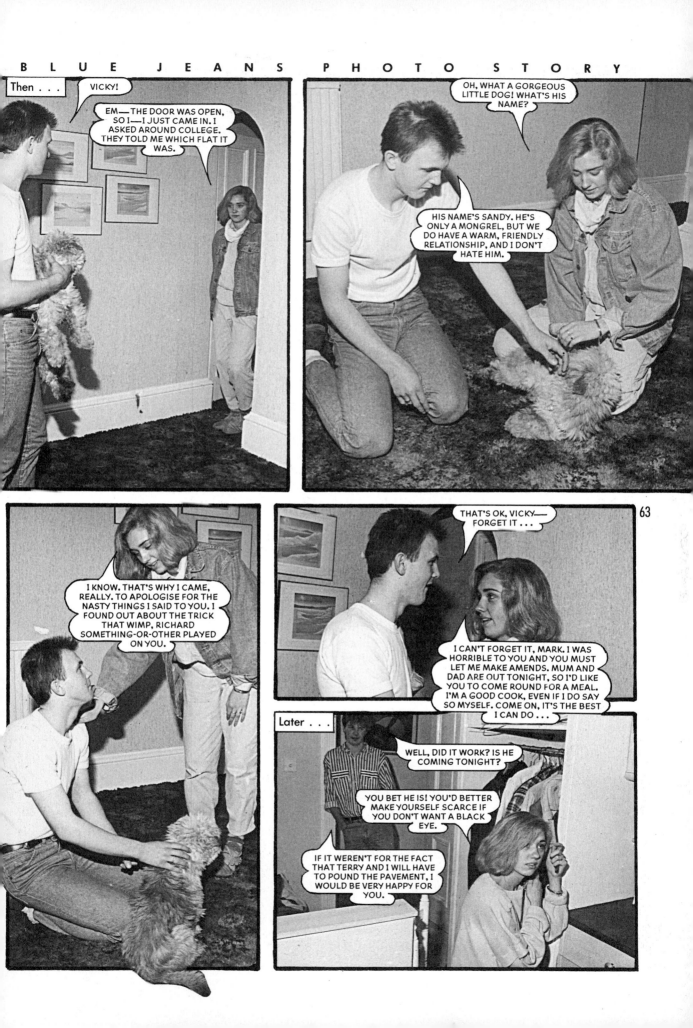

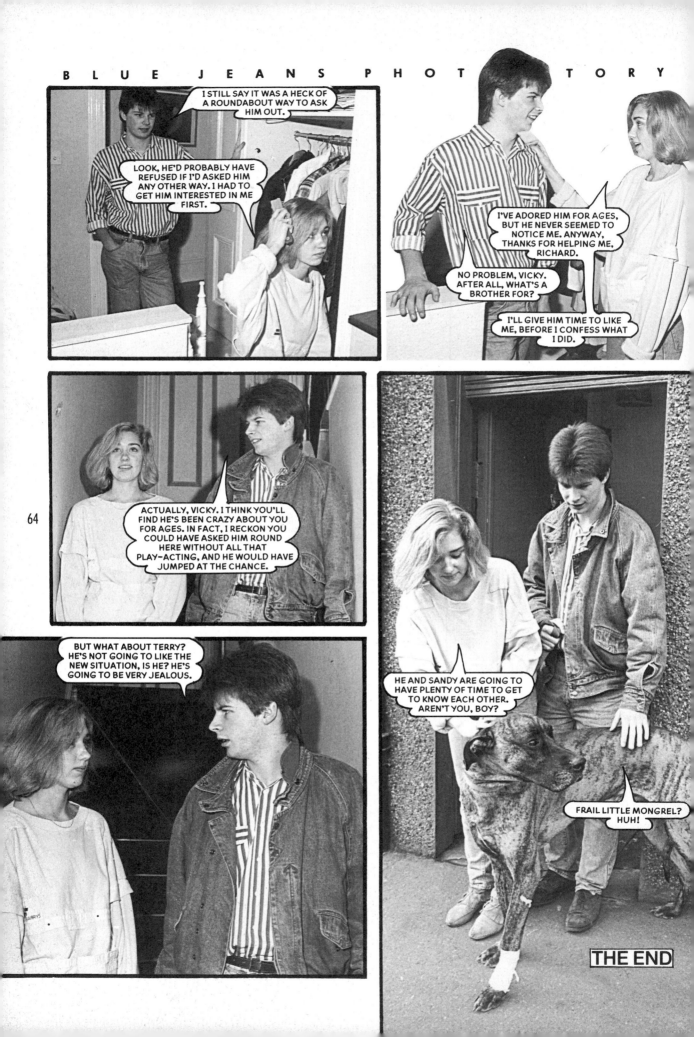

64

THE END

HUNK NO. 2:

NICK BERRY

As requested by:

Vicky Brown, Cheadle.
Pamela Milne, Kirriemuir.
Kathryn Mitchell, Reading.
Jenny Bottrill, Surrey.
Helen Prowse, Kent.
Linda Coomber, Biggleswade.
Angela Marsh, Clitheroe.
Karina Sampson, Yorkshire.
Lindsay Methven, Winscombe.

Lindsay Durrant, Essex.
Emma Davies, Mid Glamorgan.
Yvonne Johnstone, Dunfermline.
Lisa Sweet, Surrey.
Toni Powell, Northampton.
Ann Artwood, Burton-on-Trent.
Helen Cox, Nottingham.
Roisin McGarry, Belfast.
Rachel Williams, Dartford.
Kathleen Burton, Kidderminster.
Helen Walker, Cleveland.

Supplementary

BE versatile, gals! Use accessories to change your looks and liven up a limited wardrobe.

◆ Jewellery, from Wrygges.

66

◆ Shoes, from BHS. Pearls from C & A.

◆ Jumper, scarf and tights, from C & A.
Black velvet dress, from second hand shop.

◆ Yellow gear from a selection at BHS.

BENEFiTS

Scarf in hair, from C & A.

Shoes, from Saxone.

67

Necktie and collar tips, from Top Man.

◆ Green top, from C & A.
Mini, from Top Shop.

Supplementary BENEFiTS

◆ Suit, from Richard Shops. Frilly cotton shirt, bag and shoes, from C & A.

◆ Yellow silk vest and jewellery, from C & A.

■ Velvet beret, from BHS. Jewellery, from Wrygges.

◆ Yellow pumps, from Chelsea Girl.

◆ Scarf, silk skirt and extra wide belt, from Hennes. Jewellery, from craft fair.

Hat, from BHS. Jewellery, from Wrygges.

◆ Tan shoes, from Chelsea Girl.

◆ Hand-knitted cardi, from craft shop. Mustard top, skirt, tights and shoes, from Top Shop.

69

70

CREDITS
Hair and make-up: Mary-Ellen Lamb.
Hat: From a selection at The Hat
Shop.
Rugby Shirt: From the Great Universal
Stores Catalogue.
Towel, hatpin, hair band and scarf:
Beauty Ed's own.

OOD · FOR · YOU ...

en's the perfect colour, whether you nt to look cool and sophisticated, or sporty and bursting with vitality . . .

Cucumber has loads of different uses . . .

You've run out of toner? Rub a couple of slices of cucumber over your face and rinse off with lukewarm water.

It's great for sore, puffy eyes, too. Relax with a slice over each closed eye for about fifteen minutes and you should see a definite improvement.

And if you've any left after all that, you could even try eating it! As well as being extremely low in calories, cucumber's also a natural diuretic (It gives you the urge to spend a penny more often!) so it you're feeling a bit bloated — before your period, for example — it should help.

Vegetables of all kinds are an essential part of a healthy diet.

Most of them are low in calories and they really fill you up, but that doesn't mean you can ignore them if you aren't trying to lose weight. (The reason they're so filling is because they're an important source of fibre.)

Vegetables are also rich in vitamins and minerals, so it really is important to eat them regularly — at *least* one portion per day.

And don't be put off by the thought of soggy, school-dinner-style cabbage — vegetables don't have to be like that.

Crisp salads of green pepper, celery, etc. taste great and haven't had all the important elements removed by over-cooking.

We all know that apples taste nice and fresh and, like most fruits, are very good for you indeed.

But did you know that you can make a face mask for oily skin by mashing up an apple and applying the goo to your face? (Take the peel off the apple first, stupid!) Thought not!

And if your skin is dry or sensitive, try the same idea, using an avocado. This is the fruit with the highest fat content, which makes it ultra-fattening, but a great moisturiser.

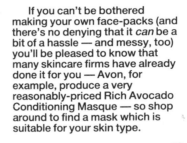

If you can't be bothered making your own face-packs (and there's no denying that it *can* be a bit of a hassle — and messy, too) you'll be pleased to know that many skincare firms have already done it for you — Avon, for example, produce a very reasonably-priced Rich Avocado Conditioning Masque — so shop around to find a mask which is suitable for your skin type.

If you tend to flush very easily, or just have a naturally high skin colour, you can cover the redness by applying a little No 7 Colour Corrective Moisturiser. Wait a few minutes then cover it with your foundation and powder in the usual way — the green moisturiser won't shine through unless you've really overdone it.

This is also an excellent way to cover broken veins or other small red marks on your face.

Green eye make-up's always popular, because it's so adaptable and you can get a wide variety of different looks with a comparatively small collection of make-up.

However, for a relatively subtle, basic look, you'll find it best to use another colour of shadow along with the green — pinkish tones, like we've used here, are particularly good.

Start by brushing a little pale green shadow over your lids and into the socket lines, then add a warm peachy-pink shadow above the green, right up to the brows, and carry the pink to the outer corners of your eyes, blending it well with the green shadow where the two colours meet.

Draw a very light line beneath your lower lashes with a brown or mossy-green pencil, and smudge it slightly to soften it.

Finish off with two coats of brown or brown/black mascara. (If you decide on brighter eye colours, you may like to try a green mascara.)

Obviously the lipstick you choose will depend on the strength of your eye make-up, but, in general, you'll find warm pink, peach and brown tones will go well with green. Red, however, isn't usually a good idea, so you're best to avoid it.

Chicago Bears Sweat Top. Track-Suit Bottoms. From all good sports shops.

American Football, James Dean and Heavy Metal A-Z Books. All from John Menzies.

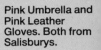

Pink Umbrella and Pink Leather Gloves. Both from Salisburys.

Boxer Shorts, from Top Man. BMX Bikin' Gloves, from British Home Stores. Football Scarf, from all good sports shops.

boys

No inspiration for the younger man in your life? Don't worry, though, you can rely on Blue Jeans every time . . .

74

"The Yellow Jersey", by Nike. Sweat Top. From all good sports shops.

Jade Cardi and Top. Blue and Green Tie. All from Top Man.

PATRIOTS 11

American Football Top. Running Shorts. From all good sports shops.

Black Leather Belt and Zeon Watch. From Top Man.

Black Lacy Tights and Black Lacy Fingerless Gloves. Both from Salisburys. Black Suede Pumps. From British Home Stores.

Red and White Stripey Nightshirt. From Top Shop.

Green and Black Scarf, Green Fingerless Gloves and Green Lace-Up Pumps. All from British Home Stores.

Black and White Clock. From British Home Stores.

girls

Gifts for chums and sisters — and not a record token amongst them . . .

75

Marilyn Monroe Book and Madonna Video. From John Menzies and all good book and video shops.

MARILYN
Mon Amour

WARNER MUSIC VIDEO

Black Bag and Black Belts. All from Salisburys.

Black and White Stripey Umbrella. From Salisburys. Socks and Bag from Top Shop.

Doors Album — for trendies everywhere. From all good record shops.

Classy Blue Necktie with Brooch. From British Home Stores.

Watch those old movies over and over again. "Wuthering Heights" and "Blue Hawaii" are just a couple of classic Videos. From good video shops.

For saucy mums . . . Black Negligée. From British Home Stores.

Flower-patterned Clock. From British Home Stores.

mums

There's more to mums than flowery shirts and multi-packs of American Tan tights . . .

Brighten up Mum's shopping trip — PVC Bag. From Salisburys.

Saucy vixtress underwear — Cami Top and Cami Knickers. Smelly Pomander. All from British Home Stores.

Ladyshave and Curling Tongs. From Boots.

Ol' Blue Eyes is still a fave with mums . . . from all good record shops.

Pink and Grey Swirly Shirt and Black Bag. From Top Shop. Pack of Three Handkerchiefs. From British Home Stores.

"Pick of Punch" Book and "Fawlty Towers" Video. From bookshops.

PICK OF PUNCH

FAWLTY TOWERS

Grey and White Stripey Shirt and Grey Tie. From Top Man.

dads

Cast those diamond-patterned socks and initialled hankies to the wind and turn your dad into a trendy with some of these . . .

77

Black Umbrella, Furry Moccasins and Suede Gloves. From British Home Stores.

Large Purple Scarf and China Trinket Box. From British Home Stores.

Make him sporty — Golfing Accessories and Darts. From all good sports shops.

Red Key-holder and Wallet. Black Passport Cover and Driving Licence Holder. From British Home Stores.

Navy Leather Handbag and Navy Gloves. From Salisburys.

Shoe Cleaning Kit and "Gentleman's Grooming Kit". From British Home Stores. Mains-operated Shaver. From Boots.

With thanks to — Salisburys, British Home Stores, Top Shop, Top Man, John Menzies, Boots and The Sports Locker, Dundee.

RUB- A- TUB- TUB!

Woo-argh! Just look at that hunky (?) body! Phil Collins in his trendy, rustic bathroom.

An early version of the bath tub. Not much room for your ducks, is there?

A more unusual use for a bath. Here we have Jean-Jaques Burnell of The Stranglers (the bare-chested one, untrendies) taking part in the annual Bath Tub Championship in the south of France.

Here it is — the first feature specially designed for reading in the bath. And if you put your annual in a plastic bag, it won't even get wet!

DIRTY BRITAIN

● In the past, some countries were much cleaner than others and, much though we're ashamed to admit it, Britain wasn't one of them.

The Greeks and the Romans were perhaps the greatest bathers of all time. The Romans built large, elaborate bath-houses incorporating steam-rooms, hot baths, cold baths and rooms to exercise and relax in. Slaves were always on hand to massage and generally pamper the bathers. At one point, there were 952 public baths in Rome.

● The Scandinavians are another clean-living lot. Their favourite form of bathing involves flicking themselves all over with birch twigs to improve the circulation, then sitting in a steam-room (this was the origin of the sauna). Afterwards, they finish off with a brisk roll in the snow! (Brr! Give us a bubble-bath any day.)

● Britons, on the other hand, used to be a right smelly bunch. After the Romans left, their bath-houses fell into decay. Most people bathed only once or twice a year and used vast amounts of perfume to try to cover up the awful smell the rest of the time. Royalty weren't much better — Queen Elizabeth I was proud to announce that she bathed four times a year "whether she needed it or not"!

TRIVIA, TRIVIA, TRIVIA, TRIVIA . . .

Here it is, fact fans, loads of useless trivia about baths to inform and amaze your friends with . . .

Did you know that . . .
. . . until 1850, soap was taxed in Britain? (A good reason for not bathing!)
. . . a bath uses 10-15 gallons of water, whereas a shower uses only 4-6?
. . . last century, Americans thought bathing was dangerous? In Boston, you needed a doctor's permission before you could step into a tub?
. . . the earliest known bath-tub is 3600 years old?
. . . according to a 1978 survey, 3% of British people never bath *or* shower?

We also carried out a BJ gang survey and you may (or may not) be interested to know that 50% of the BJ gang sing in the bath (or shower) and 50% also read in the bath (or shower, as one smart Alick put it — maybe he covers his book in cling-film).

BATHTIME BEAUTY

We all know what a hassle it is remembering to do the boring bits of a beauty routine, but if you make a point of doing them in the bath, you'll find life a whole lot easier . . .

Give yourself a manicure/pedicure while you're in the bath. The water softens the nails, making them easier to cut, and it'll be easier to push back your cuticles, too. Use a pumice stone to get rid of rough bits of skin on your feet.

Shave your legs and underarms once you've been in the bath for a few minutes. The hot water will have softened the hairs, so they'll be easier to shave and you'll be less likely to cut yourself.

If bathing dries out your skin, switch to a mild soap and put bath oil in the water. Watch out, though — oil makes the bath very slippy!

Suffering from the effects of sunburn? Then try this bathtime cure. Make a pot of tea with 1 oz. of tea, then add to the bath, stirring well. This helps burnt skin to tan rather than go red.

After bathing, roughly towel yourself dry then moisturise. The dampness of your skin will help seal in the moisturiser.

ANYONE FOR CRUSHED STRAWBERRIES?

Us common mortals may just bathe in water with a splash of bubble-bath for a special occasion, but in the past, the well-off — especially royalty — have indulged themselves in some rather odd substances . . .

Mary, Queen of Scots liked to bathe in wine. Her jailors were not amused at the large bill she ran up. Another one with more money than sense was La Belle Otero, a famous Victorian dancer. She preferred to bathe in champagne — what a waste! Cleopatra was quite well known for bathing in asses' milk, but did you know that the Empress Eugenie of France's favourite was crushed strawberries? Bleugh!

HUNK NO. 3:

ROB LOWE

As requested by:
Chris Robertson, Herts.
Rebecca Vaughan, West Midlands.
Sara Faversham, Cheshire.
Susana Fernandez, Birmingham.
Vicky Sheridan, Mid Glamorgan.
Ruth Boggs, Co. Down.
Hazel Sinclair, Shetland.
Katrina Downing, Surrey.
Madeleine Goddard, Leicester.
Carla Tivey, Leicester.

Amanda Lavelle, Birmingham.
Christine Barrass, Doncaster.
Heather Sutcliffe, Tyne & Wear.
Carol Campbell, Castlereagh.
Maire Dennis, Waterford.
Susannah Lock, Wiltshire.
Karen Beatty, Co. Derry.
Andrea Greenwood, Derbyshire.
Joanne Diamond, Cheshire.
Sarah West, Dorset.
Debs Staines, Gillingham.

Going to the local launderette was a new experience for Beth . . .

HI! BEATS 'DALLAS' ANY DAY, DOESN'T IT, WATCHING THESE MACHINES SPINNING ROUND? AH, THERE GO MY NAVY BLUE RUGGER SOCKS. AND THERE WAS I THINKING THEY'D BEEN TOTALLY DEFEATED IN THE SCRUM BY MY TEA-TOWELS.

EM, YEAH. FASCINATING.

TRUST ME TO COME DOWN HERE ON WALLIES' NIGHT. LET'S HOPE MUM GETS OUR WASHING MACHINE REPAIRED SOON . . .

Digging Your Scene

81

MY SHIRTS JUST NEED ANOTHER COUPLE OF SPINS AND THEY'LL BE FINISHED. YOU CAN HAVE FIRST REFUSAL ON MY MACHINE THEN.

OH, THANKS.

I HAVEN'T SEEN YOU DOWN HERE BEFORE.

NO, OUR MACHINE AT HOME'S BROKEN.

A few minutes later . . .

IT'S THE HIGHLIGHT OF THE WEEK FOR ME, COMING HERE. I'M OUT OF WORK, YOU SEE. BUT I'VE AN INTERVIEW TOMORROW, SO TONIGHT I'M WASHING MY FEW DECENT CLOTHES. MY NAME'S JIM, BY THE WAY. WISH ME LUCK, WON'T YOU? I HATE INTERVIEWS. I CAN NEVER THINK OF ANYTHING TO SAY.

YOU COULD'VE FOOLED ME!

EM, GOOD LUCK, JIM. OH —AND MY NAME'S BETH.

WELL, SEE YOU THEN, BETH — THANKS FOR YOUR COMPANY. IT'S BEEN GREAT LISTENING TO YOU.

'BYE, JIM.

GOOD, NOW PERHAPS I CAN CONCENTRATE ON GETTING READY FOR MY OWN INTERVIEW TOMORROW. JIM ISN'T THE ONLY ONE WHO'S OUT OF WORK!

But later . . .

OH, MUM, LOOK AT THIS! IT'S MY ONLY DECENT BLOUSE, AND IT'S STREAKED WITH BLUE. I ONLY PUT WHITE THINGS IN THE MACHINE, TOO . . .

SOMEONE MUST HAVE LEFT SOMETHING BEHIND. YOU SHOULD HAVE CHECKED. I HOPE MY SHEETS AREN'T RUINED.

CURIOSITY
KILLED
THE CAT

Julian, Ben, Nick, Migi.

CAT FACTS

● Nick used to work as a paddle-boat attendant in sunny Ibiza.

● Migi got a bit part in the movie, 'American Werewolf in London' as a punk with multi-coloured hair.

● Ben has "hippie" parents. His father is photographer, Jean Claude Volpeliere-Pierrot. His mother is a PR and stylist.

● Julian achieved a life-long ambition when the band appeared on the 'Roland Rat Show'!

● Migi wears three pairs of socks, boxer shorts and a hairband to bed!

● Nick is an avid 'EastEnders' fan.

● Ben bought his famous fisherman's cap in Greece. The others hate it — but Ben's pretty attached to it — he even claims to wear it to bed!

● Musically, the band admire Rosie Vela, The Blow Monkeys and UB40.

● Julian went to a posh public school.

● Migi used to sell Rubik's Cubes in Carnaby Street.

● Through his parents, Ben has rubbed shoulders with pop megastars like The Beatles and The Rolling Stones. He's still very friendly with Eric Clapton who he met when he was a nipper.

● The band originally had a singer who was a cross between Pete Burns and Boy George and who the others nicknamed 'Talcy Malcy'.

● Their first live show in mid 1984 was attended by Paul Young and Kid Creole.

● Ben used to be a model — he did a TV ad for the TSB and fashion modelling for Jackie magazine. He also appears on the cover of Mike Read's Pop Quiz game.

● Migi used to skip school to see punk bands like Siouxsie & The Banshees and The Damned.

● Ben starred in videos for The Thompson Twins and XTC.

● The band would love to branch out into films. They all see themselves as budding actors — except Julian, who says he's not too keen on the idea, he says he's too shy.

● Ben says 'man' all the time. (What a hippy!)

● Their full names are, Ben Volpeliere-Pierrot, Nick Thorp, Miguel Drummond and Julian Brookhouse.

● Their songs are all written with their "hidden" keyboards player, Toby Anderson.

● They all grew up within four miles of each other in London.

● Their former bands have included Twilight Children, The Anarchist Angel and The Plague.

HAPPY EVER AFTER?

I could hardly believe my luck when I met Stuart at the school disco. But I should have known it was too good to last.

"OH, you must come to the disco," the dark-haired girl said. Elaine — no, Linda, that was it. I was still finding it a job to remember names even though I'd been at Westover Comp nearly a week. There were thirty-five in our class, about fifteen more than there'd been in 4a at St Just's. "It's great," she went on. "Not like a school disco at all, if you know what I mean."

I didn't, not exactly, because St Just's had never run them — too old-fashioned I guess — but I was anxious to join in everything and not seem anti-social.

"We're all going," Elaine said. "You just come along with us. You'll like it."

So I did. And I met Stuart.

The school hall was so crowded you could hardly move, yet we just came together as if it was meant. I was leaning against the wall, watching the dancing, and right next to me was this tall, blond-haired guy. I could feel his eyes on me, and that was what had made me turn my head. We looked at each other for

quite a while, the way you do.

Then he asked me to dance and that was it really. We spent the rest of the evening together, oblivious to everything and everyone else. As the music finished and people began to drift home, Stuart asked if he could see me again. A walk in the park after school? I nodded, smiling, and I couldn't help wondering if any of the other girls in my class had noticed me and Stuart together, and if they had whether they would say anything about it — tease me a bit or something. Not that I'd mind, I was too happy.

Sure enough, when I went into the cloakroom the next morning, there was a lot of whispering going on which stopped the moment I opened the door. A little group of them turned and stared at me. I hung my coat up, waiting for them to say something and feeling a bit embarrassed when they didn't. Then I distinctly heard someone say Stuart's name, and then mine. There was a 'shush' from somebody else.

"Look," I said, finally, unable to stand it, "if you've got something to say about me I'd rather you said it to my face if you don't mind."

"You wouldn't like it," a ginger-haired girl said.

"Go on, tell her, Alison." The one standing next to her dug her in the ribs, still looking at me.

"Yes, I'd like to know," I said. I felt cornered with the four of them there, and a bit worried. I mean, a week ago I hadn't known any of them. The one called Alison put her arm round my shoulder as if she knew how lost I was feeling, and immediately I cheered up.

"You might think we're being bitchy and telling tales," she said, "but we reckon it's pretty hard being new and not knowing about Stuart McArdle." The others nodded. I didn't know what to say. I felt cold inside. The awful thing was I tried to remember Stuart's face and for some reason I couldn't. Yet walking to school this morning I'd thought of every single detail.

"YOU'D better tell me," I mumbled. I knew that I wouldn't like what was about to hear, but I had to know.

"He always goes straight after new girls," she went on. "We reckon he's got radar or something. He can't resist trying it on. Then after a couple of dates, he gives them the elbow. It happens every time."

"We're waiting for the day when some girl gets the message and turns him down," one of the others said. "Only of course they never do. They're too flattered. I mean, he is pretty good looking."

"Yes, he is," I said dully. It *had* been odd the way he'd been standing right next to me like that. Looking at me. Weighing me up. Moving in for the kill. He must have had plenty of practice.

"We hope you don't mind us tellin

you," Alison said, squeezing my shoulder. "Only we thought you ought to know."

"I asked you to, didn't I," I said. It sounded sharp, but I couldn't help it. All I wanted was to get on my own, think things out.

By the end of the day I'd decided one thing I wasn't going to do was wait around and meet Stuart. I dashed away as soon as the bell went, and was one of the first people out of the gates. The walk home was interminable. All I could think about was Stuart. Even though he was a rat, I couldn't get him out of my mind. The thought of school next day was even worse. I told myself Stuart wouldn't dare say anything, he'd realise I'd been wised up to him by the others, but I dreaded bumping into him.

NEXT morning, I dawdled around until I thought everyone would have gone to registration, but just as I stepped into the practically empty corridor I saw him leaning against a door, arms folded, obviously waiting for me.

"Right," he said, dead stonily. "So why didn't you wait for me yesterday, then?"

"You ought to know," I snapped, really stung by his attitude.

"I don't and I'd like to. I waited for ages." He glowered at me, and I glared back. Just the sight of him made me feel weak at the knees but I wasn't going to give in.

"Then you know what it feels like to be on the receiving end," I told him. "I bet all those other new girls'd give a cheer if they knew."

"You trying to be funny or something?" he said.

"Oh, get lost!" I replied, turning away. I could feel my voice breaking and no way was I going to give him the satisfaction of seeing me in tears. But as I rushed into the cloakroom I realised several of my class were still in there and must have heard every word. I knew they had when Alison's friend spoke up. "Good for you," she said in a low tone. "It's about time someone stood up to him." I wished I felt as triumphant as she obviously did.

I just felt wretched. But at least I wouldn't hear any more from him, that was for sure.

I was wrong.

Whether he couldn't bear to admit defeat or what, I don't know, but when I came out of school, Stuart was waiting for me. I simply shot past, nose in the air. I could hear him calling but I didn't stop. Once I got to the park I slowed down, thinking he'd given up, but he hadn't. An arm shot out from behind grabbing me.

"Listen to me, Keren," he began.

"No, you listen to me!" I yelled. "Just leave me alone, right? Leave me in peace, you — you rotten creep!"

He let me go then. He looked stunned — hurt. I told myself it was my imagination, but my heart nearly broke

as he turned and walked away. I *wasn't* going to be used and thrown away like an old shoe, though. I simply wasn't. He could look as sorry as he liked, but I wasn't going to join the list of his past victims.

Next morning, I found a note in my desk. Goodness knows how it got there. I opened it and it was from him, Stuart.

"Keren," it read. *"I don't know why you've changed but I haven't. Please meet me after school. Please. Stuart."*

It was that final please that really got to me. I don't know why, it just seemed touching somehow. I couldn't help feeling that surely he wouldn't have kept chasing me like this if he didn't care. I mean, if I was just a laugh, a casual date, wouldn't he have given up by now? I thought about it all day. Agonising over the 'ifs' and 'buts' and wondering what I should do.

At break, Alison came over to congratulate me on dumping Stuart. "It's the best thing that could ever have happened to him," she gloated. "That creep doesn't deserve to go out with anyone!"

I looked at her and wondered why she hated Stuart quite so much. I mean, a lot of the girls disliked him, but she seemed to have some personal vendetta going against him. Anyway, none of that mattered. I'd decided to meet Stuart after school and clear things up once and for all. I owed him that much.

"Hi, Keren," he said nervously, as he

caught sight of me at the gate. "I'm glad you came."

I was surprised at how apprehensive he was. Funny thing was, I felt a bit nervous, too. I suppose that's what made me blurt it all out, there and then. He stopped me as soon as I mentioned the girls in the cloakroom.

"Not Alison Shaw and her mates?" he groaned.

"Yes." I stared at him. "How did you know that?"

"Oh, Keren," he said. "She's my ex-girlfriend. She's got it in for me. She's determined I'll go back to her, although I never will. It was finished weeks ago."

"You mean — ? " I paused, light dawning. What an idiot I'd been, faithfully accepting everything Alison told me.

"If you'd just give me a chance," he pleaded. "I'll prove to you that everything Alison's said is a pack of lies. I'm not like that at all."

So I did.

We've been going out together for a month now, Stuart and me. It's been great, just like it ought to have been from the beginning, if I'd trusted him enough and not listened to other people. Oh, Alison and her mates don't speak to me any more, but I don't care. I've settled in with the other girls and made some real friends now.

It's funny, but when I used to read happy-ever-after romances I used to think they were a load to rubbish, life wasn't like that. But you know what? It *is*!

SHEER JEANIUS

What are 140 years old, usually blue but sometimes black or brown, rivetted at points of maximum stress and an absolute must if you're a rawk 'n' roll rebel?
Give up? Jeans, of course!

Around 1860, a small-time tailor by the name of Strauss made his first pair of working pants (as the Americans call trousers) for a goldminer in California. A few years later he added the refinement of copper rivets to reinforce the seams of the garments he sold. Almost overnight they became *the* American workwear, making Mr Strauss not only very wealthy but also very famous — his Christian name was Levi and the trousers he made were the very first Levi's.

Made of denim (so called because the material originally came from Nimes in France), jeans remained essentially workwear until the 1940s when they first became popular with women, worn baggy and rolled up to the ankles to show light or bright-coloured ankle socks. This was topped off with a large, baggy jumper known as a Sloppy Joe.

By this time many other big names like Wrangler had also cottoned on and were also making jeans. In the fifties, jeans with full-length, narrow legs started to be worn more tightly. Teamed up with a T-shirt and a leather jacket they became the

1. Mags, Pal and Morten show off the best way to wear jeans — round a hunky Scandinavian bod.

2. Rick, Francis and the lads showing what snappy dressers they were back in the seventies when men were men, flares were huge, and it was hip to flash your tum.

3. Sexy, soaraway S'manfa Fox showing that jeans that your dad wouldn't let you out of the house wearing really are fashionable.

4. Slade in the early seventies with enough spare material in the trousers to knock up a tent or two. No doubt the shoes would double as tent poles they're so high.

trade mark of the teenage rebel, played to perfection by James Dean or Marlon Brando. Although not always universal, this style has lasted right up till today.

Anybody who was fashionable in the sixties was wearing shrink-to-fit, pre-faded jeans — preferably so tight that they could only be zipped up by lying on the floor. Ouch! Some people, mainly skinheads, started to shorten the legs of their trousers to show off their enormous boots. This very macho style can also still be seen today.

In the seventies, flares reached truly enormous proportions then died a death as narrow, straight-legged jeans became popular once more.

While flares were popular, though, it was quite common to add material to make them even wider. For high street-cred, this material had to be in a different colour or even flowery-patterned if you were a hippy. The ultimate hippy gear to go with the Afghan coat was a pair of well-worn jeans, preferably patched with all sorts of different materials. A bit of tasteful (tasteless?) embroidery would top things off nicely.

At this time it was estimated that everyone in Europe and the U.S.A. under the age of 40 owned at least one pair of jeans.

The current craze for Levi's 501s revives the pre-faded, shrink-to-fit look, while the trend in ripped jeans is a godsend for people like The Ed who're too mean to buy a new pair after they've put a knee out.

While styles may come and go, jeans are always popular and fashionable which just goes to show that Mr Levi Strauss was on to a bigger goldmine than the prospector he first made trousers for.

Possibly the best known bum shot in the business. Brooocie shows how to wear red tab Levi's.

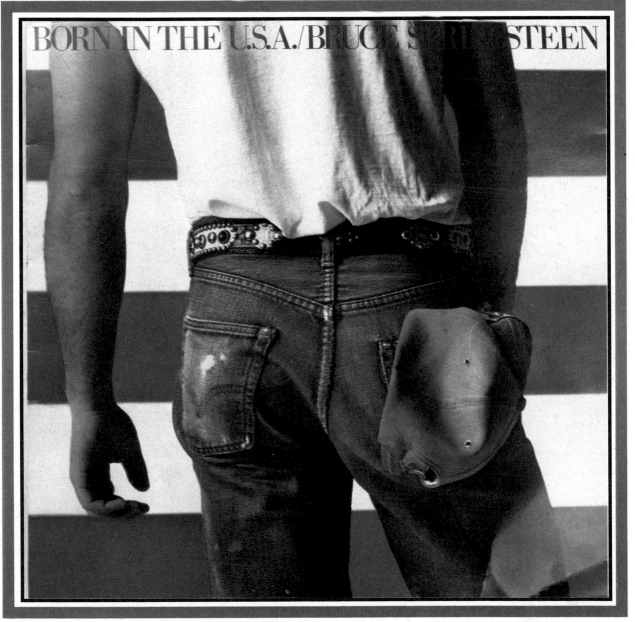

HAPPY FAMILIES?

▲ Recently, I have not been getting on with my parents. My dad's always having a go at me for no reason, and when I ask Mum to get him to stop she just says I deserve it. I'm so sick of the arguing and fighting that I feel like leaving home, and would if I had somewhere to go.
I am 14.
Nick Berry Fan, Norfolk.

Family problems are often the most difficult to solve. Unlike having an argument with a friend or a boy you only see occasionally, you've got to live with this person who annoys you so much. We offer a little advice on how to get along at home.

● Please help me. My little brother is making my life a misery. He never leaves me alone for a minute. It doesn't matter what I'm doing, he's always there making ignorant comments and trying to start fights. I try not to hit him, but sometimes I do and then I get the blame for everything even though he started the fight. Please tell me what to do. I can't stand it much longer.
Kerry, Manchester.

▲ We get several letters like this, saying "my **parents** have a go at me for no reason."

The first thing to do is examine your own behaviour. Are you **sure** you don't do anything to provoke their anger? Do you do your fair share of the housework? Is your room tidy? Do you tell your parents where you're going when you go out and come home at a reasonable hour? Do you do as you're told and try your best to avoid arguments? If you can truthfully answer yes to all these questions, then the blame obviously does not lie wholly with you.

The next time your parents "have a go at you" calmly ask them what's wrong. Perhaps you'll get a sensible answer or perhaps all you'll get is "Shut up and don't be cheeky!" Either way, stay calm. If you just get into a slanging match with them nothing will be achieved. Point out that you're not being cheeky, you'd just like to know why you're annoying them and what you can do to solve this.

With any luck, you'll be able to solve these situations by reasoned discussion. However, it's a sad fact that no matter what you do, you'll never be able to please some parents. In this case, talking it over with a friendly relative may help, but if things get bad, you can always turn to one of the organisations below for help.

92

USEFUL ADDRESSES

Citizens Advice Bureau
OR
Samaritans
Look in the phone book for the address and telephone number of your local centre.

N.S.P.C.C. (National Society for the Prevention of Cruelty to Children),
67 Saffron Hill,
London EC1N 8RS
Tel. 01 242 1626
Give help to children who are being mistreated.

● **Younger brothers and sisters** usually pose two different kinds of problems. Little brothers, once they reach the age of about 10, take a delight in irritating you, acting tough and showing off, especially in front of your friends. To you, this behaviour may seem silly and immature, but to boys of this age, it feels grown-up.

If the diplomatic approach doesn't work then there are another two methods you could try. Putting a lock on your bedroom door (with your parents' permission) is quite effective in that it gives you privacy in your own room, but remember you will still have to venture into the outside world from time to time. Discussing the problem with your parents is perhaps the most effective solution, if they are sympathetic. Detail the aspects of your brother's behaviour which irritate you (Be reasonable, though. He has as much right to live in the house as you do!) and ask them to have a word with him. Or perhaps you could encourage him to take a time-consuming hobby, such as building model aeroplanes, in the hope that this will keep him occupied!

Much of this advice also applies to **younger sisters.** However, there are one or two additional problems. Sharing a room is the cause of many an argument between sisters, but there is quite a simple solution — divide everything in half. Agree to have two walls each for your posters, divide the wardrobe space, dressing table and chest of drawers in two. Set aside times when the bedroom is yours alone for doing homework, entertaining friends, playing records, and when it is for your sister's exclusive use. Ask your parents to witness this agreement, so that there will be no arguments over what you decided later.

Another frequent moan about younger sisters is that they borrow clothes, make-up, records, etc. Agreed, this is a nuisance, but it is actually a compliment in a way. To them, you lead an exciting, grown-up life and they want to be like you.

A little understanding, rather than a screaming match, will go a long way to solving this problem. Put the best of your clothes and make-up to one side and explain to your sister that she can't borrow them. Then sort through the rest of your belongings. Are there any old clothes or make-up that you never wear and you could quite happily give to your sister? Perhaps you have some stuff that's not your 'best' but not unusable either. You could agree to lend this to your sister on the odd occasion.

Don't be totally selfish with your time either. Maybe you could reach an agreement where she doesn't pester you when you're busy, and in return you give her some advice on make-up and clothes in your spare time.

◆ **My problem is my sister. We have to share a bedroom, but she never lets me in it. She's always in there playing her records. Then, when *she* makes a mess of the bedroom, she gets *me* to clear it up. I've tried telling Mum, but she just says it's my room too, so I ought to help clear it up. What can I do? There's no way I can have a room of my own.**
Bon Jovi Fan, Kilmarnock.

◆**Older brothers and sisters** have their problems, too. A major complaint is that they get to do things you aren't allowed to. This is only natural, though, as they are older. You wouldn't expect a seven-year-old and a twelve-year-old to be treated in the same way, so neither can you expect a twelve-year-old to be given the same freedom as a seventeen-year-old. Be patient, and in time your parents will relax the rules. In fact, they might even be more lenient as they'll have learned from dealing with your older brothers or sisters.

Another difficulty is that big brothers and sisters can often be bossy and use their greater strength against you. In situations like these, there's no point in fighting back. Try to reason with them, but if that doesn't work you'll have to enlist your parents' help. Don't be put off by cries of 'tell-tale'. You're entitled to an equal say in the house, and just because they can thump you harder doesn't mean you shouldn't get it.

1

2

3

4

5

...AND

Well, how many did you recognise? Here's your chance to find out, pop parrots!

1. This was simps — I mean, how could you fail to recognise those cheek-bones? Yes, you've guessed it, it's mean and moody John Taylor.

2. He hasn't changed much, has he? He's still pretty stupid-looking. It's that wicky-wacky DJ and general pain-in-the-neck, Jonathan "I just lurve Sammy Fox" King. If you got this right, then you must be a big fan and you should be pretty ashamed of yourself.

3. Was he bald or was it just a wide hair-parting? Whatever the answer, he's definitely improved with age, hasn't he? It's former Genesis man, Peter Gabriel.

4. Lots of things have changed for the better — including this chap's dress sense. Praise the Lord! It's Levi's model and singer extraordinaire, Eddie Kidd.

5. A bit of an easy-peasy one. Yes, of course, it's Paul Young. No Blue Peter badge for you if you didn't get this one right.

6. It's the wee tartan terror himself — Stuart Adamson of Big Country. Obviously, he didn't have any ready supplies of spikey boy hair gel in those early days with The Skids.

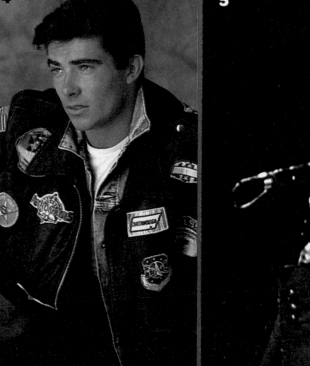